The Weight of Illusions

by

Robert Markland Smith

Dedicated to Bonnie, Isabelle and Cordelia

TABLE OF CONTENTS

ACKNOWLEDGMENTS

Some of the texts in this book were written with the financial assistance of the *Conseil des arts et des lettres du Québec*.

Being a Fool for God appeared in The Exterminating Angel Press, EAP: the Magazine.

The Train to Nowhere appeared in Lion's Head Press Magazine.

Are You Wild? appeared in Nth Position Online Magazine.

St. Thomas and Someday my Prince Will Come were published in Retort Magazine.

Cover drawing by Isabelle McLean-Smith

Desktop publishing by Cordelia McLean-Smith

Preface

I would like to present this book as a collection of stories taken from maya, gathered from illusory circumstances, and written in a frenzy of dreaming. The common thread that weaves through them is their unreality. From the French text *Les Chroniques du maya* to the somber cemetery scene in *Threnody*, the characters are watching shadows dancing on the walls of Plato's cave. If you are looking for a revelation of truth – political or metaphysical – herein, you should look elsewhere. These pages are cooked in unreal sauces and stirred by imaginary kitchen helpers.

Even the insight into truth contained in the final story *The Whole World in His Hands* would probably not pan out if tested scientifically. But the reason lies and unreality are the theme of this book is that we live in an age of disinformation – the agencies that have the mission of educating the public spread lies to justify their own ploys. Likewise, the Robin Hoods and Scarlet Pimpernels of this age are computer hackers who blow the whistle on the government and end up exiled, under house arrest or tortured in military prisons.

These heroes are not mentioned in the following pages. The totalitarian world system has shut them up, and yet they are prophets and conveyors of doubt in the Harry Potter generation. Likewise, this book is self-published for lack of a more mainstream venue. May it find you open to its hidden, occult conclusions. May its theosophy work its magic in your hearts as you read on.

Robert Markland Smith
Montreal, Quebec
February 2014

1. EULOGY FOR A HERO

One Sunday afternoon, around 1959, as we were watching television in our living room, there was a documentary about a new social phenomenon in the United States. My dad and I and the whole family were watching this show, when the camera showed a church full of people chanting, "BLACK POWA! BLACK POWA!" They looked pretty militant and determined. I don't remember what the news commentator was saying, but I was interested, having never been exposed to these ideas. Immediately, my dad jumped out of his chair and ran over to the television set and violently turned off the set. He was visibly very upset – and I didn't know why.

There were other expressions of black culture that appealed to me around that time. Little Stevie Wonder, as he was known then, was only about ten years old, when he produced a 45 r.p.m. record called "Fingertips" and my friends and I thought it was a cool song, especially since it was recorded by someone our own age.

There was a movie featuring Sidney Poitier and Tony Curtis called "The Defiant Ones," in which two prisoners escaped from jail and were handcuffed together. Sidney Poitier portrayed a black prisoner, and Tony Curtis, a white one. They had conflict which added drama to the story, but the message was that they needed each other to escape the authorities. Neither one of them could make it on his own. Symbolically, it was a message of solidarity.

In the early fifties, a North Vietnamese priest came to live at our house for nine months. Apparently, all his family had been killed by the NLF and he was studying theology at a university in Ottawa. I didn't understand what he was doing there or why he slept in my room, while I slept in the hallway. Another time, a missionary came to visit our house and described being tortured by the Chinese authorities. Also, my dad would confide in people that he had blue blood – or so he thought. It boosted his self-confidence. He had been decorated by pope Pius XII for his volunteer work in 1956, and his credentials included being royalty. He had studied for the priesthood and we never did find out why he left the orders at age 28. He was a boss in the fede ral government but they got rid of him because he didn't push his employees hard enough to produce. He was a pillar of the community, which helped me achieve in grade school.

Like all kids, I believed that my father was important. I saw him on television on a talking-heads show: he sat on a panel with a few other men and discussed ideas that were over my head when I was nine or ten years old. I idolized my father. He could do no wrong. He was, well, bigger than life.

However, my dad began disappointing me. He took me to New York, on a trip to a UN-sponsored convention about education in which he represented Canada. He took me to the offices of the United Nations, and I was allowed to sit in the spot where the Secretary of the UN, Dag Hammersholdt, meditated. We went to the Little Church around the Corner for Sunday morning mass.

But an incident happened the next time he took me on a trip to a UN-sponsored convention. He was talking to a priest, who asked him, in French, how his kids were doing in school. He must have imagined I was hard of hearing because he answered, "My daughter is doing really well, but this one here is kind of slow." I tried to protest and was hushed up in short order.

EULOGY FOR A HERO

I thought of course I was his pride and joy, because when he came home from work, I ran upstairs to his bedroom and fetched his slippers, which I put on his feet as he sat with his feet up. And he would sit me on his knee while he smoked cigarettes. I always had pulmonary diseases because of his constant smoking, like whooping cough, pneumonia, bronchitis, fevers and colds, of course. But I wanted his approval. He was my hero.

His employees would sometimes come for dinner and speak to him with deference. I certainly didn't earn respect like that from my colleagues at school. I may have been a high achiever academically, but I was useless in sports. For instance, when our class played baseball, the two best players were appointed captains of the two opposing teams. They in turn picked the best players for their teams. I was always last to be picked, right after a kid who was blind. So I wasn't very popular. There was a girl who liked me. She on the other hand was very popular. I would walk to school with her every morning and carry her schoolbooks. But when we got within a hundred and fifty feet of the schoolyard, where all her friends were watching, she would take back her books and tell me, "OK Peewee, walk fifteen paces behind me." I guess she called me Peewee because I was no giant. I was in awe of her and found her cute. I had a crush on her.

Once in a while, my mother's friend Jeanne Sauvé would come for dinner, but my sister and I were not allowed to listen in on the conversation after dinner. We had to go to bed right after supper, because my mom's friend would get into arguments with my dad. She would criticize the clergy and of course, my dad would defend the Church and there was a lot of harsh arguing going on, as my sister and I sat at the top of the stairs, listening in.

Sometimes, the Jehovah's witnesses would come knocking at our door and my dad would whip out his bible and scream at them and they would scream at him for a whole afternoon. My cousin and I would be upstairs in the bathroom looking out the window and listening to my father's apologetics.

3

What was embarrassing was that my dad knew the mass better than the priest and at Sunday mass, he would sing the Latin hymns louder than anyone else in the church and if everyone else in the parish was sitting down, my dad would insist we stand up.

After Sunday mass, we would come home to dinner and everyone would gossip about a parish member who was effeminate. "Imagine that! He lives with his parents and has his own telephone!!" Nevertheless, this guy turned out to be one of the smartest guys in the parish and got a Ph.D.; he became a professor at the University of Ottawa.

Sometimes on Saturday afternoon, dad would take me to do the stations of the cross with him. And when he reached the twelfth station, where Jesus is crucified, my dad would extend his arms as though he was crucified also, and he would gush with tears. I wondered what was wrong with him.

If I got in trouble – for instance if a neighbour saw me smoking cigarettes with my friends, and reported it to my mother – my mother would side with me and tell the neighbour to mind his own business. But if I got into trouble and my father heard about it, he would go one step further and denounce me to the authorities.

One day, I asked my uncle what he thought about my father. He replied, "Robert, your dad has a heart of gold, but he is so narrow-minded that he can see through a keyhole with both eyes." On the Lord's day, if the neighbours were mowing their lawns, he would pace back and forth in our house, while he would scream insanely, "Those Protestants are mowing their lawns on Sunday!!"

Yet I wanted dad to be my friend. Once, he took me fishing and another time, he went into the backyard and threw the football around with me. I was very proud that day. And every school day, he would help me learn my catechism lessons.

I felt a deep loneliness because I knew my father didn't understand certain things. One day when I was nine years old, he overheard me saying the word 'fuck' while talking with my friends. So he took me into his office, which was at the back of the house, and did a crude drawing of a penis. He explained to me what he knew about procreation. He said that when the penis gets hard, it ejaculates a little man into the vagina of the woman. I giggled at first, but then I got really fascinated. And when the lesson was over, he advised me never to say the word 'fuck,' because only sailors say that. So I was privileged because now I knew something that my friends did not know.

I had mixed feelings. My dad was the door to privilege. On the other hand, his religious views were an embarrassment. A kid wants to feel cool. Parents always embarrass their children. Kids understand right away in life what is cool and how to be cool. But parents and other adults are always an obstacle to gaining cool points.

Kids are very conformist, especially when they are nine or ten. But when Elvis appeared on the Ed Sullivan show, my dad turned off the tv set again even though the camera blocked Elvis's gyrating pelvis. I wanted to see Elvis, because everyone liked him. My dad had another agenda. No sex! No gyrating pelvises! My son wasn't going to get corrupted right in our own living room.

It wasn't easy. There was no one to talk to about this. I certainly wasn't going to talk to a priest about it. After dad died, the whole family agreed he was in heaven! There wasn't anything I could say to anyone. Everyone knew he was a saint.

EPILOGUE

Recently, my family doctor and I were discussing my dad, and she told me, in French, "Listen, Mr Smith, your father didn't pull those ideas out of a hat. Those were the ideas that were prevalent in the thirties in Quebec." My father was influenced by Lionel Groulx, who was a leading intellectual among the French Canadians during my dad's formative years. And being raised in a monastery, he never did go through adolescence properly. Any kind of rebellion or protest was strictly taboo. He felt he had to defend the Church against its many enemies. Today, I certainly wouldn't want my own children to get corrupted either. And if I have a resentment against my father, I did have a part to play in that conflict. I am not sure the baby boomers have solved any of the problems we were protesting about back then. "O brave new world, that has such people in it."

December 9, 2013

2. PEACE THAT PASSETH ALL UNDERSTANDING

It was one of those lives. My husband was in the hospital, freaking out and bouncing off the walls. He had gone off his medication a few months before, and had gone out of his mind. Mad as a hatter. Mad as birds.

The kids were young and it probably affected them for life. One day, Nathalie, the younger daughter, said to me, as we were walking down the street, "Daddy's not nice anymore. Now there is only you that's nice." He would take the kids in the car, driving erratically, driving up one way streets the wrong way, and screaming, "That goddamn wife! That goddamn wife!" So I would hide the car keys on him behind the washing machine in the basement. He would scream that someone kept breaking into our house and stealing his car keys. He would stay up at night, playing bizarre videos and records that kept the kids awake. He had lost all sense of affection and slapped the kids. One time, Nathalie cut herself because she had been jumping up and down on the bed, an accident happened and she had to go to the hospital for stitches and he refused to visit her in the children's hospital, no doubt because he didn't want to get hospitalized, claiming it was "a science fiction hospital." He would walk out of the house, leaving the front door wide open. And he went into rants about his

7

late father, who had also been mentally ill. For hours on end, he would demonize him and accuse him of having been an undercover nazi or of having worked for the police.

Not knowing what else to do, even though he was not a drinker, I went to a meeting of Al Anon one evening, and that was helpful. However, there wasn't much humour or levity in the air. This was a roomful of victims. They discussed how they didn't get involved in their husbands' madness or projections. They had to ward off the blows of their alcoholic partners. I didn't have much of a support group otherwise. There was Angela and there was Beatrice. There was Susan and Karen. But none of them had offspring. They didn't understand what I was going through with my husband. My husband also projected on me, falsely accusing me of listening in on his phone calls. He threatened to get physically abusive and screamed a lot around the house.

This scared the kids, and I knew I had to get him committed. I went to the clinic and made an appointment with his nurse, behind his back. She understood, as this had happened previously. He had developed mental illness when he was a young adult and had been seen at the same clinic for over twenty years. He was almost perfect as long as he took his neuroleptic meds, but when he thought he was cured and didn't take his pills anymore, he would gradually get sick. I told the nurse what he was doing, and she was familiar with his pattern. She took care of everything. We met at the courthouse one cool November morning, as agreed, and I testified before an old judge that my husband needed to be hospitalized. I was very, very nervous. But the judge seemed to be a compassionate man and issued a court order, which is the only way to get a relative hospitalized in this country, and I was told what to do. I had to wait for a time when my husband would be home, and call an ambulance. Then I had to show the paramedics the court order, and they would take him to a psychiatric hospital by ambulance. It all went smoothly, although my husband was furious with me and kept a grudge for a long time that I had curtailed his freedom. I had no choice. He was a threat to the kids.

This was wearing me down and I developed insomnia, just because of my anxiety level, living with a time bomb. Once he was hospitalized, it meant I became a single mom for as long as he was locked up. I hadn't worked in a couple of years and knew I had to go back to work. I was going to be the sole breadwinner for a while.

But first, a miracle happened – well, pretty good synchronicity. A couple of days after he got committed, I was relieved that the nightmare was over – he was temporarily out of the picture. Now, I went to the grocery store to buy some milk for the kids. And suddenly, I realized I had no cash in my bank account and no credit on my VISA card. What was I going to do!!? I came home and thought about it for about five minutes. The kids were at school. None of my friends had any money. All of a sudden, the phone rang. It was a lady from city hall. I wasn't expecting any calls. She said, in French, "Hello, my name is Lise Leclerc. I am calling from Montreal City Hall. Is this Kathy McGuire?" I said I was. And yes, I was a translator. I had worked in that field for twenty years, except for the past couple of years. She went on. "Your husband's cousin gave us your name. We have a temporary job for you, replacing a translator on sick leave. Would you like to start work on Monday?" I said I would. She said there was a formality. Would I go in the next day and write a translation exam from French to English? Yes, I would. It was all set. The next day, I wrote and passed the exam with flying colours. This was on a Friday. The following Monday, I started working. It was too good to be true!

At first, this was tricky. I was alone with the kids. My two daughters were eight and six, and in no way autonomous. I was stuck with the proverbial double burden of home and work.

I woke up early, and had to get the kids up by 5:00 o'clock to get them ready for pre-school. Sometimes they didn't feel like waking up so early, and I had to insist. I had to run a tight ship. In a way, it was simple: there was one single chain of command. My husband wasn't around, sabotaging my plans with his illness. I just couldn't think about him at this point. I had to temporarily shut him out to survive and take care of the kids. Luckily, my daughters were obedient. They knew something was wrong, because daddy wasn't there, but their insecurity made them cling to me and depend on me. I generally didn' t have to repeat myself. The children knew I meant business.

On the other hand, I had no time for other people. My attitude was, "If you can help me, stick around. If you are going to be a nuisance, get lost." When I went shopping with my daughters, I expected old ladies to hold the door for us! I had to cut out all social amenities. I had to push to get through the day. One time, I was short thirty-five dollars to buy a pair of shoes for my other daughter, Madeleine, and I walked into my accountant's office and told him bluntly to give me the money. He is not one to be charitable, but he knew I was desperate. I was serious. He reached into his pocket and gave me the cash.

I had one speed. It was "go." Sometimes, it was "faster." I couldn't let the kids do nonsense. If we had to leave for school at 7:15, I couldn't let them slow us down. They had to have their boots on and their hats and coats on by 7:15. There was zero tolerance for fighting or fussing.

I would make the kids' breakfast, made sure they brushed their teeth and combed their hair. Then their clothes and school uniforms had to be ready, ironed and washed. Their homework had to be done. And then we would walk half a mile to their school. I dropped them off at pre-school, which started at 7:30. Then I walked one block over, took the bus to the metro station, and sat on the metro for half an hour, so I would arrive at work at city hall on time by 8:30 a.m.

Every minute counted, every second was calculated. However, there were some pleasant fun times thrown into the week. Sometimes, at night, after all their homework was done, we would have activities to entertain them. For instance, we would cut up words out of the newspaper and put them into a hat; then we would in turn pick out words and make up poems and glue the words to a piece of paper. And every evening, I would read them a story from a book before they fell asleep. There were several libraries nearby, and on Saturday afternoons, after the grocery order was done, we would go to the library together. We would borrow amazing kids' books for bedtime reading. I was hoping they would develop a taste for literature later on in life. At one point, I had to cancel the cable TV subscription, because they had stopped reading and were watching too much television. Instead, I bought them all the Harry Potter books, and they read them all. This got them interested in reading. When I read them bedtime stories, Nathalie, the youngest one, would often disrupt and start laughing and fooling around. It was a struggle to be patient.

Every now and then, they would be invited to a friend's birthday party. This meant buying an appropriate present and getting them there on time. It also might mean socializing with other mothers and comparing notes on raising kids. I could also discuss childrearing with my colleagues at city hall. Many of the secretaries and clerical workers there were single moms also. There was an amazing degree of solidarity among us. Once in a while, we would have a coffee break together or eat lunch in a group at the restaurant. It wasn't all desperate being a single mom. However, what I didn't agree with at city hall was the racism against a Haitian woman who worked with us. The other employees felt the food she brought in for her lunch smelled spicy and they would gossip behind her back. And I felt some of the other employees discriminated against me because I had an English-sounding name.

Every penny counted, and I couldn't afford babysitters very often. I rarely used the car and took public transportation as often as possible. Gas is expensive. We didn' t eat expensive cheese or cakes. We were still eating meat back then, so that added to the grocery bill. I didn't drink, so there was no alcohol to pay for in the bill. One thing that cost me was doing the laundry, because we didn't own our own washer or dryer. We lived in a high-rise and had to use the machines in the basement. It cost to wash as well as to dry the clothes. Plus it meant taking several trips on the elevator.

I tried to train the children to clean up after themselves, but I don't think I did a very good job of it. They would rarely help with the dishes either. You can't raise perfect kids.

Once a week, on Sundays, we would go visit my husband at the psych ward for an hour. For the longest time, he wasn't getting any better. But I felt it was important that the children see their father, so they would learn compassion and visiting people who are sick. Also they had bonded with him and I wanted them to stay close to him. It wasn't always easy. Sometimes, he would just be angry with me because I got a court order and got him committed. Other times, he would respond to the kids' attention.

I took naps whenever I could. I would get very tired from being on the go all the time. I had no problem falling asleep at night now that I was a single mom, thank god. There was no more stress caused by my husband's antics. I burned up my energy every day and it didn' t take long to fall asleep. The kids also slept well, although Nathalie sometimes wet her bed, and that meant changing the sheets in the middle of the night. I bought them native dream catchers and hung them over their beds, so they fell asleep easily. This reassured them.

This routine went on for about six months, into the following summer. Everything went smoothly. However one morning I was especially tired and got on the subway as usual, went two stops and suddenly, I spaced out. I asked myself why I was doing this, and got off the metro. As soon as I stepped out on the platform, I realized this was a mistake and waited for the next subway to come. But for a split second, I just snapped. I couldn't take the pressure anymore. That day, I was a bit late for work.

I had never realized how much was involved in raising

kids, because I had to do everything myself. For example, they regularly grew out of their clothes. It was a lucky thing I could give Nathalie her older sister's hand-me-down clothes, but still it was expensive. Oftentimes, there was no extra money left over. They each had their own bed, which my husband had bought. They didn't have any bicycles. That year, they had adequate winter clothes and skates. On weekends, they sometimes went skating at the community arena. There weren't many accidents. One time Nathalie cut her face while jumping on the bed, but that was before their father was hospitalized. They did catch strepthroat and that involved taking a few days off from school and going to the clinic, but using antibiotics, they recovered promptly. My boss also gave me time off to mind the kids at home.

My older sister, who lives in Ottawa, came for a visit one day and brought the kids presents. I am pretty close to her but she was very busy with her career at that time. Her children were grown up and living on their own. She had a boyfriend called Michel who made the kids laugh with his constant jokes. She came here on a Saturday and Michel did the driving. They stayed a whole afternoon and my sister told me that if I needed anything, to let her know. She was very fond of my kids and I knew she was a responsible woman.

The kids' marks were good in school, although Nathalie's teacher commented that my daughter disrupted the class by chatting with her neighbour. Madeleine was supposedly a quiet child who never said a word in class. Her teachers loved her because she was a serious student and kept her notebooks tidy.

I would finish work at 4:30, take the metro and a bus to the kids' school and pick them up at 5:30 at after-school. The workers made sure the kids did their homework during this session, which facilitated things for me. We would walk home and have supper. I found however the school nickel-and-dimed us for pizza lunch, and other programs that came up regularly. And I had to pay for the daycare services before and after classes.

By summertime, there were a couple of events at school, like graduation, the end-of-the-year concert and a party in the schoolyard that I had to attend. But now it was time for summer camp. I had saved up to pay for them to attend camp for six weeks. Plus their grandmother bought them clothes and new sleeping bags for camp. After a week of preparations, I drove them to the mall, where all the kids' parents waited for the school buses to arrive. As usual, the buses were late. My kids had proper suitcases and sleeping bags and were thrilled to get aboard the bus. They were supposed to come back home every two weeks and stay in the country in Rawdon for most of the summer. At that time, in 2001, it cost me fifteen hundred dollars to ship them off to camp. And their grandmother chipped in about three hundred for the clothing and sleeping bags. The camp was called Trail's End Camp. It was your low-budget all-purpose summer camp.

In June that year, the employee I had been replacing came back to work from her sick leave. She had had a colon operation which consisted in shortening her intestine. I was notified my term was over.

Right away, I started looking for federal government contracts and landed a short-term job, working out of my office at home.

My husband was recovering, according to the doctors at the psych ward.

My situation was developing. Now one Saturday morning, I had been busy with the translation contract, when I felt chest pains. There was difficulty breathing. My chest felt tight. This lasted about from 10:30 in the morning until noon. By twelve o'clock, my lungs felt like they were on fire. I was also getting increasingly anxious. At 12:15, I finally called for an ambulance. It arrived within thirteen minutes, with the sirens blaring.

The paramedics came into my apartment on the sixth floor wearing their purple and gray uniforms. They were big husky guys. There was something military about their appearance, but I trusted them. They took my blood pressure and pulse. Then they took my temperature. I told them my lungs were burning. They asked me if I felt pain in my shoulders and arms. I said no. Had I thrown up? No. Had I been drinking? No. I asked them if I was having a heart attack and they replied that maybe so, but only a blood test at the hospital would determine that, because when you are having a heart attack, there is a certain enzyme present in your blood. I told them I was willing to go to the emergency ward. They were very professional about it. They brought in a yellow stretcher and lay me down on it. They tied my hands on my chest with straps and put a blanket over me. Afterwards, they gave me some aspirin to swallow and made me breathe oxygen through a tube that they inserted into my nose. Finally, they gave me a couple of puffs of nitroglycerine, which I took under my tongue. I was in a panic, because I was in a lot of pain, and everything had become extremely intense. But I trusted the paramedics. They knew what they were doing. And they took me to the Verdun Hospital.

· · ·

I remember seeing a pile of dung and a flurry of flies buzzing furiously and feverishly all around it. I remember seeing a whirlwind of dead coloured leaves spinning around, blown by the wild autumn wind. I remember being in the middle of a riot and wondering what I was doing there, as people were running to and fro, as the police charged through the crowd on their motorcycles.

Once we got to the hospital, I got rushed through triage and ushered on a stretcher into the emergency ward, where there were constantly over six nurses puncturing holes in my arms, making me snort nitroglycerine, giving me aspirin to chew, while oxygen kept flowing into my nose through a plastic tube.

Finally, I saw a cardiologist, a man called Dr Maranda, who was over six foot five, and he told me I had had an infarctus. The pain gradually subsided, as well as the level of intensity. I was eventually left alone, with tubes coming out of my arms and nose, hooked up to a monitor that recorded my pulse and blood pressure. After a while, the nurses came to see me occasionally to take my blood pressure and make sure everything was all right. These women were very supportive, although they were under a lot of pressure at work. I wasn't the only patient there, and whenever I spoke to a doctor or a nurse, kindness was practised.

I started looking around at my surroundings. There was a curtain that they could wrap around my bed, going around a track on the ceiling. There was an old man in the bed next to mine, judging by his voice, although I couldn't see him. On the other side, there was a teenager covered in tattoos, sleeping with tubes also coming out of him. Both patients were white. There were about thirty or forty other patients in the ward, but I couldn't see them. The nurses, orderlies, doctors, cleaners and other staff kept parading past my bed, in and out of the glassed in nursing station. Behind the glass pànel, I could see but couldn't hear the staff sitting down and talking on the phone, reading charts, going about their business.

You couldn't sleep. There was always someone waking you up.

After a couple of days, I was in the intensive care unit, in a room by myself. This was a big relief. I still had slight pain in my chest. I was provided with a phone and called a couple of people. My sister sent me a bouquet of flowers, which the staff kindly placed in a vase. There was a note from her saying that she would come to Montreal and take care of my kids for me. I was so grateful, because that was a big worry. For the time being, Madeleine and Nathalie were at summer camp. But then what? My older sister took the kids to Ottawa with her eventually, long enough for me to recover from this heart attack.

I met with an older male cardiologist called Dr Malo, who told me I had been lucky to survive this heart attack. He said one of my major arteries was blocked and I would need an angioplasty. He kindly explained the procedure to me: the doctor in the operating room at Notre-Dame Hospital would go in through my wrist, where he would make a small incision, and drive a wire up to my chest and place a crutch called a "stent" into the blocked artery to

Power, the force that kept me alive. Mind you, the next thought was: when is going to be my next heart attack? Will the next one be fatal? This thought gave me a tight chest. I still had plenty of anxiety. And I needed to find peace.

I had arrived back home. I made myself a sandwich, out of the leftovers in the fridge. I didn't feel like cooking very much. As a matter of fact, I didn't feel very motivated to do anything. My little walk to the church had drained me physically, although I felt inspired to research spirituality. I decided to take a nap.

I had a dreamless sleep and when I woke up, the sun was shining on me through the window facing west. I blinked and blinked again. At least the sun wasn't hard to figure out. It was always there. I felt energy once again. The sleep had given me strength.

It seemed like just a couple of weeks before, I had been rushing off to work at city hall. I missed the kids. I thought about my husband. Was I going to take him back? That was a big question. It sure was a chore raising kids by myself. But he was sick in the head, I thought. Was it safe? I postponed thinking about this. I would go for counselling on this issue.

I drifted off to sleep again, in and out of a fantasy. And that is how the days went on, for a few weeks. I felt thrilled to be out of the hospital, I loved the sunshine and fresh air, I would look at the blue summer sky and see the birds circling around, and it all felt great, but I was so small, and so weak. Basically, I felt glad to be alive, which I hadn't felt in years. I had been on a treadmill for several months. Suddenly, I started thinking there was a meaning in my life. I was receiving some kind of grace, and it seemed urgent to find out about this power that was waking me up spiritually.

. . .

I discovered Emily Carr. One day, a few weeks after I went to church, I decided to go to the library. It was in the afternoon, and great streaks of gray light came shooting through the large windows of the building, as I browsed the stacks, looking mainly at picture books. I found two or three large books containing colourful paintings by Emily Carr, the artist of British Columbia. As soon as I looked at her depictions of the forests out West, with their great swirls of energy rushing from the ground to the sky, colour patterns around the great trees, I had a direct response, a gut reaction, identifying immediately with this woman, at a deep primitive level. I sat down with a couple of these books at a table and read about the serpentine force, a power the Theosophists had felt coming out of the Earth. This was contact with the Goddess, I thought, and perhaps this was a clue to my recovery.

I browsed in the library's computers and borrowed a couple of books by Theosophists, from around 1900. There was a book called Esoteric Christianity, by an author I didn't know called Annie Besant. There was another book by a fellow called Ledbeater, about the chakras, but this struck me as flaky. And there was a book by Madame Blavatsky, but I never opened it once I got back home.

I remember the part in the book by Annie Besant where she discussed the "kaw," which is what remains of a person's soul on earth after they die. It can be felt for a few days.

This led me to return to the library a couple of days later and do research on authors like Carl Jung, Wilhelm Reich and R.D. Laing. I read parts of books by Jung and one whole book by Reich called *The Murder of Christ*, and these spoke to me. I felt Reich was in touch with the psychic energy in the universe. He called it the orgone, I believe. He believed in the genital embrace, as opposed to crude sex. I didn't have the courage to read the entire huge volume entitled *The Mass Psychology of Fascism*, but I glanced at it.

All this reading took up a lot of time and energy. I thought also of going back to work, when I received a translation contract from an agency in Toronto. It had been about a month since I had worked, and I honestly believed I could do this work. The job involved a collective agreement between hotel employees and management. I did a few paragraphs, but had to stop. I felt bad for the client, because they really trusted me. However, I felt chest pains and that was a wake-up call to stop working. The people in Toronto were not amused, but the manager of the agency understood. Her secretary thought I was being a wimp. They never gave me work again…

I was flat on my back again until late August, when my kids finished their stay at summer camp. It was arranged with my sister that she would mind them until I was back on my feet. I spoke to them on the phone, and they were worried about me. They wanted to know how their father was. But I told them they could trust my sister to take care of them.

Meanwhile, I had multiple appointments with cardiologists, who prescribed pills and more pills. One doctor had me run on a treadmill, but she determined I did not have angina. Nevertheless, I was given a dispenser of nitroglycerine in case I couldn't breathe and thought I was having a second infarctus. These appointments took a lot of energy and taxed me emotionally and physically.

The amount of walking I did helped a bit, and I was gradually getting stronger. I still had the services of "meals-on-wheels" and the women who delivered the meals were very sweet. But I realized I might have to stay on welfare for the time being. I took my pills religiously. And I reported to the cardiologists every couple of weeks.

Throughout this period, I felt blessed. There is no other word for it. I did feel grateful, and the professionals I dealt with were very kind. I was discovering the big picture, because I thought about things. Sometimes, I would lie awake at night, and invoke the Goddess. Other times, I would pray to Jesus. I also read part of the Upanishads, and discovered the Buddha. His parables spoke to me, and I felt sustained spiritually whenever I opened a book about him.

I hadn't had time to read much during the whole period when I was raising my children, except for their textbooks and the children's literature I read them at night. This was like a vacation. I dreamed I was running, running at full speed, over trees and obstacles like rocks. I was running, and just enjoying the race. I wasn't going anywhere. Just running.

And I kept thinking about the spiritual paintings of Emily Carr, and sometimes I felt swept away by their force. "La force tellurique," as they called it in French: the serpentine force. I definitely felt carried during these few weeks.

Whenever I thought about single mothers, about divorced women, I had a sense of sisterhood. We definitely had a bond together, which was stronger than oppression or death.

I remembered something my daughter Nathalie had told me one day, when she was in my arms. We had been waiting for her sister one afternoon. Madeleine was supposed to arrive on the little yellow school bus. It was winter and I had pointed out the sunset and purple and gold clouds on the horizon. I told Nathalie, "See? That is what God looks like." She had answered me, with her high, squeaky voice, "Can God sometimes look like a little girl?" I thought about it for a minute and had replied, "Yes, Nathalie, sometimes God can look like a little girl…"

· · ·

Altogether, I spent about two or three months recovering from my heart attack. Meanwhile my kids stayed with my sister in Ottawa. She had registered them in a school near her place and they were doing just fine. I was relieved that they didn't lose a grade because of changing schools. I talked to them almost every day once they came back from summer camp, I missed them, but also appreciated the rest I was getting from the rat race. During this period, I learned that each day was different, and to take it one day at a time. I read a lot, went for short walks and then longer walks, looked at the trees and the flowers and the clouds, talked to my friends and enjoyed my life a bit more every day. I had learned to stop and smell the roses, rather than running constantly, like a hamster in a cage. I found peace of mind.

Meanwhile, I was out and about sometimes during rush hour, when all the people in the neighbourhood were going off to work. One day, I stood on a bridge over an expressway and watched a hundred thousand drivers driving in a hundred thousand cars going off to a hundred thousand meaningless jobs. All for what? For money. You could see the pollution in the air on top of the city: a big dirty, yellow and gray cloud. I wondered if it was all worth it. I knew how these people lived, the empty lives they lived. They came home from work and watched television after supper. It seemed like a big waste of time.

I kept going to the library and the museum and wandering around like a homeless person. I felt peaceful all right, but there was something missing. First of all, my kids were in Ottawa with my sister. But it was more than that. I needed a purpose. We all know about evolution, we know the human race and the entire universe are growing, from century to century, from millenium to millenium. And one evening, I asked myself, Should the entire city, the entire civilization go on strike? Should we stop everything? Should we do like the hippies and live like vegetables and just smoke pot?

I thought about this for a couple of days, for a week or two. And then it occurred to me that no, we carry on. We put our shoulder to the wheel and push – one day at a time, we try to solve the social problems, we make the effort to improve our lot and the lot of our fellow human being. I thought of all the possible situations, and it seemed that mine was not so bad. This meant there was a meaning to all the efforts being made worldwide. The wheels of industry had to keep churning out products and services. The government had to keep charging taxes. The writers and artists had to keep producing works of beauty and meaning and truth.

And we all had to help each other out, each person in their own little way. We were all in this together. We were not islands.

I was determined to recover from my heart attack, and I was going to start living my life again, but wide awake. I was going to remember these few weeks of rest and recovery. I was going to remember what I had learned.

First of all, although pacing myself and listening for any possible chest pains, I started cleaning up our house. Bit by bit, room by room, I tidied up. It took me a few days, at a slow pace. And I found I got stronger by making an effort.

Then I made arrangements to go visit my kids in Ottawa at my sister's house. Within a couple of days, I took the car and drove there. Madeleine and Nathalie were happy to see me. They wanted to know everything I had been doing. They were concerned about their father but I reassured them he was all right. I spent about three days at my sister's house. Finally, it was agreed that they would finish the school year in Ottawa and then I would take them back. I would visit like this on a regular basis. My sister wanted to make sure I got a lot of rest.

As for my husband, I decided not to take him back. I was better off alone than taking care of him. And it was the right decision. He got worse instead of better. Once he got out of the hospital, he went off his medication again. This time he did not recover. I saw him occasionally, first of all in court during the divorce procedures and later on, I met him a couple of times over coffee. He was still bitter that I had gotten him hospitalized, plus he imagined other things. He was full of resentment and I had no time for this.

It was terrible I had lost my husband, because once upon a time we loved each other. But he chose a path I couldn't follow. I felt guilty for dumping him for a few months, but it took him years to recover.

Life went on and I found serenity. I remember going on top of the mountain that is in the middle of Montreal, Mount Royal, and looking at the horizon. I had found faith, faith in a higher power, faith in life, and faith in myself. With this came peace, the peace that passeth all understanding.

Nov. 27, 2013

3. MRS. VARGAS' LITTLE GIRL SANDY

"Mais où sont les neiges d'antan?"
-François Villon, *Ballade des dames du temps jadis*

When I was a young man, I met the beautiful Sandy in a church prayer meeting in a village in California. I was instantly attracted to her and despite my recent conversion and rebirth, I attended that church every Sunday in order to get closer to the coveted lady. However, she was also interested in several men in the parish. She was playing the odds and used her beauty to wrap men around her little finger.

We had both been baptized in the Spirit and were on fire for God. This was the bottom line, but there were also hormones at work and the preachers couldn't control our instincts.

I worked on a Christian farm a few miles away. But wait a minute – before I go on, let me tell you who I am. I am a Canadian, from Montreal, Quebec and already had a bachelor's degree in French literature by the time I met Sandy. I had read about bohemian living in university, and had taken to the streets when I became old enough to assert myself. This led me to a cult in Colorado and thence, into the hands of the born-again Christians. This was 1975, and it was summertime. I had been living in a residence in Berkeley, when I was shipped out to Kelseyville, where I lived with an older couple called Bev and Mike. They had tenants there who were probably sent there by the court and social services. I worked the farm with another French Canadian fellow called Yves. And on Sundays, after milking the cows, I would head out to the neighbouring village, where I met Sandy.

I would write naïve Christian poetry and show it to Sandy, and she would exclaim, "Dat's so purty, brotha Bawb!" Before getting religion, she had been involved in drugs and crime, whereas for me it was drugs and then revolution. She was young, in her mid-twenties, and we were the same age. Her long black hair poured down on her shoulders and she looked Spanish.

One night, she invited me for supper at her house. We ended up spending the whole night talking. For a brief moment, she slept in the bedroom, and I slept on the sofa in the living room — when suddenly, while I was fast asleep, I was thrown out of bed, physically lifted and then thrown flat on my face on the floor, while a voice screamed in my head, "If you don't repent of this blasphemy, how can I save you?" Of course, I wrongly assumed this was from God and was pretty shaken up. (Even the bible says the devil can appear as an angel of light.) Nevertheless, I didn't leave Sandy's house. It was eleven or twelve p.m. and Sandy had been awakened by all the racket. We decided to spend the night talking. She told me about her friends, and that they were thieves and rode motorcycles. I told her about getting beaten up by the police when I was doing revolution. We had both repented of all these things.

However, at one point, I walked into a room, and she was lying on her back, smiling at me with her arms out open, ready to embrace me. For a split second, I was tempted, but nothing happened. And we talked and talked until the dawn.

Around seven in the morning, one of the Christian men from her church came and pounded on the door. What was this? He assumed right away what had transpired and told me I had to leave. He thought he was protecting Sandy's purity. And Sandy and I had been found out! We sat on the curb outside her house, waiting for Mike to come pick me up and beautiful Sandy kissed me on the cheek and smiled at me. But we knew the relationship was over.

Mike told me I was kicked off the farm. He told me this with indignation in his voice. And I returned to Berkeley by bus, ashamed and exiled from Kelseyville.

Basically, I had a broken heart. I remembered Sandy Vargas for many months afterwards. *Mais où sont les neiges d'antan?*

September 29, 2013

4. BEING A FOOL FOR GOD

In memory of my friend Martha Shepherd

This is a true story. Honest. Cross my heart.

My wife goes to Catholic mass once a week, even though she is a Protestant. She is very afraid of being found out. So she always keeps a low profile in church, lest she attract some undue attention or censorship. Especially because she is not a baptized Catholic and is not allowed – technically – to receive Holy Communion. She practically hides behind tall people in her pew so the priest won't see her.

I rarely go to church, any church, but I was getting rather zealous lately and wanted to go to Saint Joseph's Oratory, so I could get cured of my arthritis. I am expecting two knee replacements within a year from now. After all, there are thousands of crutches hanging on the walls of this shrine, where Brother André supposedly healed people.

OK, so this is the premiss. Today Bonnie and I decided to go to the Shrine and hear mass at 4:30. There was a mass scheduled at that time, and we arrived in the chapel right in the nick of time.

However, I noticed the priest entered the chapel alone. He was wearing a green garment, which symbolizes hope. (I know this because I used to be an altar boy fifty years ago and was taught by nuns.) He entered alone, without an altar boy. So immediately, I took initiative and did what I had seen my father do many times. I leapt out of my pew, left my cane with my wife, and marched up the aisle like a man with a mission. I walked up the steps to the altar and quietly asked the priest if he needed an altar boy. He mumbled, "Later." So I stood there beside the altar, waiting for my cue.

It came time for the reading, but I didn't know how to do this. After all, I am not an ordained deacon! So the officiating priest read the Scriptures and I stood there behind him, on one leg, on the other leg, shifting, because I left my cane in my pew.

Suddenly, like in a James Bond movie, a security guard walks up to me and grabs me by the arm and tells me to come with him and escorts me out the back of the chapel. I am trying to amuse him, saying I haven't done this in fifty years, but he is not smiling. Not only he walks me out of the chapel, but down one hall through the sacristy where there are two other men, and down a flight of stairs. I am hobbling to keep up with him, because for one thing I am sixty-four years old and for another thing, I have arthritis in my knees, but I am keeping up with him. He takes me into a back room where there is a bloody crucifix of the last guy they beat up, and by fuck, I know now they mean business.

OK, they are standing around me, and the guy who grabbed my arm is especially in my face. I can see they think I meant to steal the Host to do a black mass, or something criminal, or something equally naughty – but they don't believe my story for a minute. You wanted to sit in for the altar boy? Oh sure! Well, there is the altar boy over there and he was late… Would you like us to call the police?? Then you'll have problems! They'll teach you not to fuck with the Church!

Mind you, I didn't take a shower this morning and am missing a few teeth – so I definitely look like a homeless person in need of trouble.

I ask them if I can go back into the chapel to finish

hearing mass and could I fetch my cane? They ask me where is my cane? With my wife. Where is your wife?? At brother André's tomb? No, she is in the pew on the right and she is wearing a black coat.

They go get her and SHE IS EMBARRASSED. This is the worst possible scenario! She mumbles nervously that I meant well and just wanted to sit in for the altar boy.

They escort us to the back door of Saint Joseph's Oratory and slam the door behind us.

I guess the road to hell is indeed paved with good intentions and I can see now why my friend Danuta said to me one day, "I like Jesus but I don't like the social machinery of the Church."

In any case, it will be a frosty Friday in hell before I go to church again. Now it might be my imagination, but I could swear my knees are getting better tonight.

November 15, 2012

5. ARE YOU WILD?

By now it is 1985, and you are 36 years old - are you wild? Is that what you do, keep a perpetual hard-on all day long? You are living in a two-room basement apartment, after getting out of jail, and you have a social worker called Daniel, who takes you out to the movies, to concerts, for meals. Daniel is French from France, and you don't really respect him, because he said some racist things about blacks. He is a theology student who doesn't know God, who has theories about everything, and he is pretty much of a wimp, as far as you are concerned.

Anyway, one day, he brings his girlfriend, Bianca, along with him on one of his visits to your apartment. It is summertime, and sweltering hot. You are showing her your writings, and she tells you she is a fan of Henry Miller's. She is Italian, but speaks English to you; she has blue eyes, and short-cropped dirty blonde hair. (You wouldn't kick her out of bed for eating crackers.) Anyway, she is one way while Daniel is around. They visit for a few hours, and you serve them something to drink.

The next time you hear from Daniel and Bianca, they are at the airport, and they are off to Cuba or somewhere, and they phone you to say goodbye. You are flirting with Bianca, telling her something about getting a suntan all over. She seems to like you, but it is understood she is

Daniel's girl.

A couple of days later, someone knocks at your door. You are in your kitchen, and you go answer the door. It is Bianca. You are all flustered, because she is throwing a curve at you. You serve her a coffee, and at one point, you are both standing close to each other in the small kitchen, and she brushes against you. You take the cue, and you wrap your arms around her and kiss her, a long, passionate, wet, French kiss, her tongue in your mouth, licking your tongue and palate, like a giant snake entering a cave. When the kiss subsides, you smile at her and ask, "What about Daniel?" And she replies with a wink, "Daniel is only Daniel."

And the roller coaster rides begins. You are living on the corner of Fullum and Sherbrooke, near the old Parthenais prison, and she lives fifteen miles away, in Montreal North. It turns out she has two daughters, one fifteen and the youngest one about eight, and they don't notice you at all. Lovers come and go. Bianca tells you, with an insane laugh, that she has the forty-eight hour syndrome - a new lover every forty-eight hours. You are drinking champagne together. She tells you she is fond of corruption, and she says it with a passion. She is addicted to cocaine, or in the process of getting addicted. She is pretty wild. She works at a dating agency, a legitimate dating agency in the heart of downtown. You go see her at work, and you draw portraits of her and her assistant, who is also Italian.

Bianca is pathetic however. She was living in France at one time, when her first husband decided to sail across the Atlantic Ocean. He bought a sailboat, and took off. Well, he disappeared. Bianca spent five years looking for him. She went up and down the coast of Africa, and heard rumours and tried to keep track of where he had last been seen. But after five years of absence, he was considered missing and dead. Then she remarried three times and got divorced three times. She collected husbands, and now she has the forty-eight hour syndrome.

So you take twenty-dollar taxi rides to her house in Montreal North, and you spend extravagantly together.

ARE YOU WILD ?

One time, you are in an outdoor terrace of a restaurant in Montreal North in the hot sun, and she asks you coyly, "What are you staring at?" And you answer, "I was looking at your breast." So she pulls her right breast out of her dress, out of her bra, and lets it hang out where you can see it, right in the middle of the restaurant. You laugh insanely, she laughs insanely, and this is what kind of person Bianca is.

And there are plenty of hot, torrid afternoons, in your warm basement apartment, making love passionately on a sofa bed which falls down one time, and that is funny, and you remember that the sex is so hot and passionate, and the summer is so intense, that her black eye liner and mascara are dripping down her face, in streams of sweat, like a big black spider with its claws rolling down her cheeks. And she asks you, after about three hours of wild balling, "Is that what you do? Do you keep a perpetual hard-on all the time?" And in those days, especially if you smoked a joint, you never go soft, and Bianca and you make love until you get sore. And that is the essence of this relationship, and you tell Daniel you are fucking his girlfriend, and he is not too amused, but Bianca doesn't care about him. Daniel thought he was doing you a favour by taking you out, because you have a mental illness. But he is definitely out of the picture. You have cut his grass, mister.

And the party with Bianca goes on, for about three weeks, and it is fast-paced, and wild, and steamy. One day, however, you go by yourself to see a movie called Birdie, which sets you off. It is about a Vietnam veteran who is totally gauche with women, and has never had a girlfriend, and when he ends up in a psych ward, he thinks he is a bird, and perches naked on his bed. And this sets off a neurosis in you. You write a letter to Bianca. The letter says very weird things about women. Bianca is turned off. She tells you it is over. You try to phone her once or twice, but she won't take the call. The party is over, and she has found someone else to replace you. The forty-eight hour syndrome. You feel sad, and bitter. You hear from a friend of hers that she got married again for the fifth time about a year later. This friend is a jazz singer called Ming Lee, and he is in touch with her. You move to Fredericton, New Brunswick, that summer.

"Do you remember, baby, last September, how you held me tight each and every night, and you'll find somebody new, and baby, we'll say we're through, and you won't matter anymore." Later, that summer, you are in Ottawa, visiting your parents, and you go for a beer with your dad in a crowded downtown bar, and the Buddy Holly song is playing on the PA system, and your dad tells you, in French, "That is the tragedy of life, that relationships don't last."

February, 2014

6. RÊVE MÉDIÉVAL

Je dors. Je suis en Italie, et j'arrive à un carrefour, où les digues sont défoncées et les eaux emmurées se déversent à torrent dans les rues, coulent comme une explosion d'eau entre les bâtiments de couleur crème, et les rues sont inondées. Il y a de l'eau partout, et pour traverser la rue, il faut sauter d'une roche à l'autre. J'ai les souliers tout trempés, et je dois prendre garde de ne pas être emporté par le courant. Ces eaux sont vives et pleines d'imagination. Tout est créé subitement par ces eaux qui descendent comme des chutes d'images et de métaphores et d'étoiles.

Je me retourne dans mon lit. Je vois ma conjointe qui dort la bouche ouverte, elle ronfle et elle aussi se tourne de l'autre côté. Entre les rideaux, du fond de la pénombre, j'entrevois la lune qui me fait un clin d'œil parmi les nuages sorciers. De longs filaments gris recouvrent la planète nocturne, et je me sens inspiré.

Notre chat se promène sur le clavier de mon ordi, en faisant cliqueter les touches. Il faut se lever et le sortir de la chambre à coucher. Je me lève. J'allume dans le corridor et je vais m'assurer que les enfants dorment bien dans leur lit, en sécurité. Il y a des ombres de part et d'autre, mais tout est en ordre. Je retourne me coucher.

Comment tout cela a-t-il commencé? Pourquoi me suis-

39

je retrouvé dans cette situation, à Montréal, au fond de la nuit? Nous sommes au début du troisième millénaire, au Moyen-Âge, faut-il dire, si l'on croit les journaux. Tout est encore primitif, malgré notre impression d'être précipité dans une nouvelle époque postmoderne. J'entends une sirène de patrouille de police, comme un dinosaure qui terrorise le quartier.

Par où commencer mon récit?

. . .

Quant à moi, j'ai des souvenirs qui remontent loin. «J'ai plus de souvenirs que si j'avais mille ans.»

J'ai treize ans. Je suis pensionnaire au Petit Séminaire d'Ottawa depuis quelques mois et je suis à la maison pour les vacances de Noël. Je me trouve au salon avec ma mère, qui me présente à son amie Paule. Je la trouve jolie – alors je m'enfuis en courant hors du salon. Plein d'émotions vives et chaudes que je ne comprends pas et qui m'étouffent comme une couronne d'épines.

Maintenant j'ai dix-huit ans et je suis encore vierge. J'habite chez ma nouvelle blonde, Joan. Nous habitons à St-Thomas, Ontario, chez son oncle et sa tante. Eux sont couchés et dorment au deuxième étage. Joan tente de m'initier à la sexualité. Nous sommes seuls dans la cuisine, et elle m'a déculotté et je suis bandé. Elle me touche, elle me serre dans son poing, et moi je suis angoissé. C'est ma première fois. Je transpire. Je gémis. Mais elle, qui a plus d'expérience que moi, se rend compte à quel point je ne suis pas prêt pour elle. Nous ne parlons pas. Tout est très intense, mais elle lâche prise et s'éloigne de moi. Ce que je veux le plus, c'est ce qui me dérange le plus. J'ai une vraie carcasse émotive, comme dirait Wilhelm Reich. «Ma sale petite éducation catholique.»

À vingt-trois ans, avec une autre femme de mon âge, Lorraine, je voyage en Europe et nous baisons trois ou quatre fois par jour, entre deux visites au musée. Notre amour est entièrement charnel. Je ne la connais pas plus qu'il ne faut. Nous passons des heures à refaire les mêmes gestes, la pénétration dans une position puis l'autre puis une autre. Nous tentons des expériences éternelles, qui ne durent que des siècles et des siècles, amen. C'est ce qu'Angéline Neveu appelait du «sexe tarte à la crème». Toujours ce même rythme, ces mêmes seins, ce même pénis, ces mêmes fesses. Les petites chambres d'hôtel qui suintent de transpiration, pendant tout un été, en France, en Espagne, en Allemagne de l'Ouest, en Italie. On ne se tanne jamais de l'un l'autre, cette perpétuelle curiosité naturelle. Et nous jouissons.

Puis, rien pendant environ huit ans. Des sectes. De la science occulte puis de la religion fondamentaliste, intégriste. Toute mon énergie sexuelle est sublimée dans la prière et l'aplatventrisme. Je vais du Colorado à la Californie. Je deviens prédicateur de coin de rue. Je vise la pureté. Je suis chaste pendant des années d'affilée. On me convainc de me sevrer de mes médicaments et je sombre en psychose. Je suis suivi par des soucoupes volantes. Les appareils de télévision me regardent. Je vois des signes partout. Le délire total. Les gens qui m'entourent font des commentaires et je sais qu'on parle de moi. Tout est différent et j'habite une autre planète. Entre-temps, je lis Annie Besant, Ledbeater, Aleister Crowley à l'occasion. Ça, c'est quand je n'approfondis pas la Bible. Je me sens persécuté chaque fois que quelqu'un mentionne le mot «cul» ou «merde». Je rêve de sainteté.

Toute ma famille est d'accord pour dire que je suis très malade.

Puis de nouveau le sexe. Cette fois, je travaille dans les bureaux et j'ai du fric. Cette fois-ci c'est les putes. Une, deux fois par semaine. Parfois, deux femmes de vingt ans en même temps. Je suis ivre, je bois, je baise, je suis parfois plein de remords et je vais à la confesse. Alors je suis en mode de repentir pendant un jour ou deux – puis je téléphone de nouveau une agence d'escortes puis une autre et une autre. De temps à autre j'ai une petite copine, mais ça ne dure jamais. De nouveau, les agences d'escortes. Les longues attentes éternelles entre le coup de téléphone et l'arrivée de la «call-girl». Je suis très confus. Je ne me comprends plus. C'est l'addiction sexuelle. C'est les maladies vénériennes. Le brûlement quand j'urine. La pénicilline. Et je recommence. Des centaines et des centaines d'escortes. Des dizaines de milliers de dollars. Et toujours le remords et cette angoisse, au fond de la solitude. Au fond de la nuit.

La chevauchée des fantasmes ne dure qu'un instant. Une vie, à peine. Je m'avoue perdu. Pendant ces années-là, je ne me connais pas. D'un côté, un sorcier qui dit dix, de l'autre côté, une sorcière qui répond trois. Puis il dit neuf et elle répond quatre. Et un éclair me passe à travers le cerveau. Je suis définitivement possédé.

Je passe des années dans les bars, dans les tavernes, dans les boîtes de nuit. J'écoute du jazz. Je connais tous les musiciens. Je fume de la mari avec eux à la pause.

Je passe environ deux ans de ma vie à l'asile. Des médicaments forts. Des camisoles de force. Parfois des séjours de trois ou quatre mois à la fois. Des compagnons sympathiques, parfois des infirmiers sympathiques aussi. Parfois pas. L'isolement de ma famille et de mes amis. Une fois je serai catatonique pendant six semaines et je ne parle pas. Je ne bouge pas. On m'emmène à la toilette en chaise roulante. J'imagine qu'on veut m'assassiner et se servir de mon cadavre à des fins diaboliques. On veut mettre une enregistreuse dans ma tête et me faire prononcer des discours comme l'antéchrist. C'est la fin du monde, absolument, et je suis responsable de la Troisième Guerre mondiale. 0

D'autres fois, je pars. J'occupe un emploi, j'ai une chambre. Puis je pars sur le pouce. Je couche dans les fossés le long de la route. Je couche dans les toilettes publiques, dans les Rocheuses, au fond de l'Ontario, n'importe où sauf ici. Je m'évade de Dieu. Je m'enfuis. Lui me retrouve tout le temps. À la croisée des routes, dans le fin fond des bois, dans un poste de police, loin loin de ceux que je connais.

Entre-temps, que faisais-tu, toi qui couches à côté de moi ce soir, tandis que dorment nos enfants? La lune me le dira. Le hurlement des sirènes d'ambulance me le révélera. Mais qui es-tu, toi ma conjointe?

RÊVE MÉDIÉVAL

Une grande soif d'Amour. Un besoin assoiffé de l'Infini. Un dieu qui se manifeste seulement quand il veut et à qui il veut bien se manifester. Tiens, le voici.

. . .

Entre-temps, que faisais-tu Danielle? De quelle campagne innocente t'ais-je tirée? Combien travaillais-tu tous les jours de la semaine?

Elle, ma conjointe, venait d'une famille de trois garçons, et je ne sais d'où elle a invoqué ses idées pures, sans malice. On m'a déjà dit que sa famille l'avait mise à l'écart toute sa vie. Son frère, par contre, m'affirmait qu'elle ne voulait rien savoir d'eux. Enfin, elle m'a dit que chaque fois qu'elle essayait de s'éloigner de sa famille, on la ramenait toujours au bercail. Elle n'avait jamais réussi à s'émanciper de son père ou de sa mère.

Quand je l'ai rencontrée au début, elle habitait à deux coins de rue de sa mère et travaillait à l'entreprise familiale. Et dieu sait combien elle travaillait! Six jours par semaine. Puis les dimanches, elle faisait du bénévolat auprès des non-voyants. Elle faisait des haltères et du jogging. Elle mangeait environ cinq cents calories par jour, pas plus. Son repas du soir était composé d'un peu de pâte salée et d'un café. Elle ne portait pas une once de gras autour de la taille. Elle ne fumait pas, elle ne buvait pas. En outre, elle était maniaco-dépressive. Parfois elle était survoltée. D'autres fois, elle s'isolait dans sa chambre à coucher avec des revues d'art et de culture. Ses sautes d'humeur pouvaient passer de l'exaltation totale et hystérique à la dépression larmoyante qui durait des semaines entières.

Évidemment, on ne faisait pas bon ménage. Les premières années, on se chicanait sans cesse. Mais quand il s'agissait de faire l'amour, ça durait toute la nuit. Danielle voyait des couleurs lorsque nous baisions, elle hallucinait naturellement. Moi, je jouissais physiquement. On dit que les hommes cherchent le sexe dans l'amour et les femmes cherchent l'inverse.

Un soir, je voulais en avoir le cœur net. Je voulais savoir si elle m'aimait vraiment. Elle dormait dur. Et je lui ai demandé : «Danielle, est-ce que tu m'aimes vraiment?» Elle de me répondre : «Voui.» J'étais enchanté. J'avais cherché à obtenir l'amour d'une femme depuis bien des années. J'avais cherché cet amour partout ailleurs sauf dans une relation amoureuse. Alors je me suis dit que je resterais avec Danielle pour de bon.

Or, au début je me préparais à déménager chez elle à la campagne, mais c'est elle qui a posé le premier geste. Un jour où je ne m'y attendais pas, elle est arrivée avec ses valises dans mon logement. Il y a de cela vingt-deux ans maintenant. Mais l'histoire ne finit pas là.

Voici, elle avait un plan. D'abord, elle m'a convaincu de cesser de fumer. Je fumais deux gros paquets par jour. Pour cesser, je suis resté ivre mort pendant six mois. Chaque fois que je voulais une cigarette, je prenais une autre bière. Évidemment, j'ai gagné quarante livres. Mais je n'ai pas fumé depuis. Et aujourd'hui je ne bois pas. Tout le monde m'encourageait à cesser de fumer. Et Danielle a réussi. Effectivement, j'ai cessé. D'abord on a une douleur atroce au cerveau. Le cerveau se dégrise. On a la tête comme un fil électrique sans caoutchouc autour. Mais j'ai passé à travers.

Deuxièmement, Danielle voulait m'éloigner de mes mauvais compagnons. Ça aussi, elle l'a fait. Nous avons déménagé en banlieue, à Notre-Dame-de-Grâce, loin des bars du centre-ville et de mes amis ivrognes et sorciers. Plus de débauche possible.

Ensuite, elle voulait faire un enfant. Puis un deuxième. Chaque fois qu'on marchait dans la rue et qu'on voyait un bébé, elle me le signalait. «Regarde donc, Robert, combien cet enfant est beau!» Et oui, j'ai succombé. Un soir qu'on faisait l'amour, j'ai décidé, en deux secondes, qu'on ferait un enfant. J'ai enlevé le condom et en effet, elle est tombée enceinte.

Puis elle voulait que je travaille. Eh bien un vendredi matin, lorsque Danielle était enceinte depuis trois mois, je reçois un coup de téléphone de Moncton. «Bonjour, Monsieur Smith. Je vous appelle du Secrétariat d'État, à Moncton. Combien soumissionnez-vous pour traduire 47

500 mots?» J'ai répondu quinze cents du mot. La dame me répond : «C'est bien. Vous aurez le texte lundi matin.» Et j'ai travaillé. On a pu acheter bien des choses avec cet argent. Il y a eu, ensuite, d'autres contrats de traduction, pendant toute la grossesse de Danielle. Heureusement, le débit de travail a cessé une fois qu'elle a accouché, en raison d'événements politiques, et j'ai pu passer beaucoup de temps avec mes enfants. Car nous avons deux filles, qui ont actuellement dix-huit et vingt ans.

J'ai vu combien Danielle était brave. Le soir qu'elle a commencé à avoir des contractions, le taxi vers l'hôpital n'est jamais venu; alors Danielle a pris l'auto avec moi et elle a conduit environ cinq milles jusqu'à l'hôpital pour aller mettre au monde son enfant.

Les accouchements ont été longs. Vingt-six heures et vingt-deux heures, respectivement. Mais «la joie venait toujours après la peine» sur le pont Mirabeau. Et nos enfants étaient normaux, ce qu'on ne peut pas tenir pour acquis. J'avais déjà créée des liens avec notre premier enfant avant sa naissance. Lorsqu'Isabelle était dans le sein de sa mère, je lui parlais. Elle savait qui j'étais. Une minute après sa naissance, elle m'a fixé dans les yeux et a saisi mon indexe avec son petit poing de nouveau-né. Les liens étaient déjà créés.

À la longue, Danielle et moi sommes devenus amis. Nous avons cessé de nous chicaner. Aujourd'hui il est rare que les étincelles revolent. Nous avons tellement vécu d'événements extraordinaires ensemble que nous sommes maintenant un couple – comme si nous étions mariés!

Ce soir, je me souviens de plusieurs de ces histoires rocambolesques. Nous avons enterré mes parents, puis ses parents à elle. Tout le monde faisait du Alzheimer. Ma famille était à Ottawa, et toute ma parenté est décédée. Danielle a encore deux frères, avec lesquels elle n'a pas beaucoup de commerce, ainsi que de nombreux cousins et de nombreuses cousines. J'ai un cousin à Longueuil et ma sœur à Ottawa. Nous les voyons rarement.

Nous avons fait des voyages ensemble, parfois seuls, parfois avec les enfants. Nos enfants ont grandi et aujourd'hui nos filles sont toutes les deux à l'université.

Puis j'ai eu des problèmes de santé. Un infarctus. De la fibrillation auriculaire. Du diabète. De l'arthrite. Cela a signifié de longues nuits à l'Urgence. Je suis connu dans plusieurs hôpitaux de la région. Beaucoup de voyages en ambulance. De longues convalescences. Et Danielle a toujours été présente au cours de ces déboires. J'ai aussi reçu la visite de beaucoup d'amis à l'hôpital. Et le temps était long. Très long.

Aujourd'hui, veut veut pas, je suis presque retraité. Je suis dépassé par la technologie moderne. De plus en plus de cabinets de traduction utilisent des logiciels de traduction que je ne comprends pas. On m'a mis en veilleuse, comme un vieux cheval qui ne sert plus à rien. Mais Danielle m'assure qu'elle m'aime encore.

Le chemin de fer va loin. Il y a deux rails parallèles qui vont jusqu'à l'horizon. Déjà ma conjointe et moi nous manquons l'un l'autre, sachant bien que nous allons mourir un jour. Un partira, l'autre restera. Probablement. Et nous vivons un jour à la fois. Nous avons enterré presque tous nos amis et en avons perdu de vue. Parfois, rarement, nous nous sommes brouillés avec des gens qui ne nous parlent plus. Mais les deux rails parallèles ne dévient pas. Elles sont fidèles. Le chemin de fer va très loin.

Le 15 décembre 2012

7. SOMEDAY MY PRINCE
WILL COME

I had been in Douglas Psychiatric Center for several weeks, and it was during the October crisis in 1970. My friend Alex Duarte had gotten a day pass to take me out for a walk. It was a few weeks after the actual crisis and Alex took me out that morning to see all the Canadian soldiers occupying the city. The sky was gray, there was a cold breeze, and no one on the streets. We went near Montreal city hall, and there were troops stationed with machine guns all around the building. They were in uniform, wearing battle gear but there was no battle. It was what Trudeau called an "apprehended insurrection," and the province of Quebec was under arrest, under the War Measures Act. At every government building, there were soldiers standing erect, at attention position.

It was a Sunday morning, and behind city hall, near the metro station, we were walking around thinking over what had transpired. I was all screwed up on largactyl, on a massive dose of neuroleptic medication, when we bumped into a few comrades of mine from the *Front de libération du Québec*, girls and guys, maybe four or five of them, whom I had met that fall while going to demonstrations and riots and attending cell meetings. They were perhaps twenty years old. I was twenty-one, and when they saw how

47

frozen I looked from the shoulders on up, one of the ladies said to me, "Y t'ont pas manqué, hein?" which would translate as "they really nailed you to a cross, eh?" I was telling them that I was a patient in the College and was out on a day pass. I could barely talk. Society was brainwashing me. If the doctors couldn't give me a lobotomy, they reached the same effect of total compliance by injecting me with massive doses of medication. There was no apprehended insurrection in sight, only soldiers paranoid as hell and expecting a jack-in-the-box to spring out of the sidewalks.

I looked up and saw the oppressive skyline of downtown Montreal against a sky as gray as a machine gun or a prison wall.

All civil rights were cut off for five months and people were getting arrested and interrogated for no reason. Alex's friend Barry is a painter and he had a book on cubism in his apartment, so when the soldiers raided his apartment, they thought the book was about Cuba. Anyone left of center was denounced, arrested and checked. I know a waitress who had a black boyfriend and she was arrested for suspicion.

Democracy used a fascist law, a wartime law, to protect itself and enforce conformity. There were no more bombs, no more demonstrations, no more windows smashed. This was law and order.

I looked up at the sky and a few seagulls landed beside us, squawking, demanding food, protesting.

April 13, 2013

8. ST. THOMAS

"God is alive / Magic is afoot"
- Leonard Cohen

Very strange things were happening in 1967, in my life anyway. People I knew were experimenting with substances, psychedelic art and magical thinking. A new spiritual dimension was manifesting, and it wasn't based on established religion. What came out of this was the New Age philosophy, but this movement didn't exist yet. Also, concern for the environment, the spread of the feminist movement and the rise of black power marked the age.

Like many teenagers – I was 18 that year – I wasn't all that aware of what I was getting into, and I can't say I was really politicized. I knew there was an evil war going on in Vietnam, but I was naive about it, as well as about everything else.

For instance, one night a bunch of us ended up at Dennis's house, in Westhaven Village, in NDG, and we had been smoking a lot of pot. I was lying on the floor, in a bag, next to a lady called Joan, who I thought was Dave W.'s girl. Then suddenly, out of the blue, she and I started necking furiously, madly, in total oblivion of circumstances or convention. This went on for an eternity or two, and then I fell asleep. I crashed.

Now, while I was sleeping, some weird things happened.

THE WEIGHT OF ILLUSIONS

A guy called Phil and another guy called Peter were in the kitchen, talking, when they both felt the presence of a third person in the room, although they couldn't see anybody there. Other people, who were sleeping on the floor of the living-room, saw a shadow of a man, a transparency, wearing a fedora hat and an overcoat, standing by the door, looking at the people strewn about on the floor. I believe the next day, Dave W. told me he saw this. And I also heard about the third person's vibes in the kitchen.

Later on, I asked Dave W. if he was still going out with Joan, and he said that it was okay, I could go out with her.

However, that summer, I had finished second year at Loyola College, had worked at the NFB washing cars for two months, and had made reservations to fly to Europe for two months with a student travel agency. It was going to be low budget. Anyway, the first day I arrived in London, I stood by Cleopatra's Needle, along the River Thames, and wondered what the hell I was doing in Europe, five thousand miles away from my new girlfriend and my new crowd of friends in Montreal.

That summer, I travelled through England, France, West Germany and Spain. I would stay in rooming houses and sometimes I didn't eat. But let me fast forward here. When I returned from Europe, two months later, in August 1967, everything blew my mind. I went to the coffee shop where we all hung out, Godot's, and everyone was raving about Sergeant Pepper's Lonely Hearts Club Band, and I had no idea what this was about. Several of my friends had grown their hair long, and then it blew my mind to hear that Joan had flown the coop. I phoned her parents in Ville Saint-Laurent, and they told me she had moved to St. Thomas, Ontario. Hmm. What was going on here?

I contacted her, and she invited me to go out there and join her. Now St. Thomas is a village near London, Ontario, in the Niagara Peninsula. It is very pretty there, and sufficiently remote to be safe from what was happening in Montreal. Joan told me she had moved out there to stay with her uncle and aunt, because she didn't want anything to do with psychedelics and all the trips going down in the big city. Basically, she fled for her life.

First, I took a train to St. Thomas, fell asleep and missed my stop. I got off at London, and began to hitchhike to St. Thomas. I got a ride with a crazy, angry couple, whose car broke down about a mile out of London, and the husband turned around to me and yelled, 'None of this would have happened if we hadn't picked you up!! GET OUT AND WALK!' So as their engine was smoking, I took my grip and began to walk. Then I got a ride with a pickup truck, and the driver asked me if I wanted a job... He told me where to show up.

I remember arriving in St. Thomas safely, and joining Joan, her uncle and aunt and a bunch of the local people. I didn't know yet why Joan had moved out there – I thought she was pregnant – and I got paranoid – I thought the people there believed I was the father of the child – and finally, I was given a bed to sleep in or rather a sofa, in the living-room of the uncle and aunt.

As it turns out, I did show up for work, and couldn't handle it. It was doing road construction. First, they had me operating a jack hammer, or rather the jack hammer was operating me, bouncing me around all over the highway, and I am a little guy, not built to handle heavy machinery. The next day, I was knee-deep in mud, shoveling mud out of a pit. And finally, the gruff, tough and elderly foreman yelled at me, 'Look, get out of here! This isn't an old folks' home!' And I came back home, to Joan and her uncle and aunt, and I hadn't been fired from too many jobs in my life, and that evening, on the front balcony, I broke down and sobbed. Joan wasn't sure about me at this point.

This is where it got psychic. While her relatives were sleeping upstairs, Joan would come down to the living-room, and began initiating me to sex. I was a virgin. At first, it was traumatic. But eventually, we fell further and further in love.

Her uncle started talking about polstergeists, and how spontaneous fires appear around the house when there is a virgin present, but he was probably pulling my leg. Then everyone started noticing the psychic connection between Joan and me: she would pick a card out of the deck, and I could always guess which card it was. Likewise, I would pick a card, and she could guess. I wasn't prepared for any of this. In my bag, I had a copy of Thus Spake Zarathustra, by Nietzsche, and The Trial, by Kafka, which I was reading for the fourth time. I thought I was an atheist in those days. Joan wasn't too impressed by Nietzsche, because she opened his book at random to a passage that read, Women are at best cows. And her uncle would ridicule Bob Dylan, whom we both liked, because he said Dylan couldn't play harmonica.

One day, Joan and I had a disagreement, and she went storming off; however, I knew exactly where to find her, and wandered into a nearby park – where she was hiding, behind bushes.

Joan one day decided to take me to see a fortune teller, an old lady who lived alone on the outskirts of town. This old lady didn't know me from Adam. She sat me down and looked at my palms: she said I wasn't a worker and that I was a student. Then she guessed I was going out with a red-haired girl. Correct. Then she said, N, D, S, L. Pick a letter, so I picked S, and she said to me, in her gentle old voice, they call you 'Smitty' – don't they? (Meanwhile, Joan and her aunt were parked outdoors.) She was right – people used to call me Smitty. Then she went into a trance, and moaned that she saw a key. She added that I would live until the age of 93, and would eat some corned beef and cabbage – and fall asleep, dead. (I never eat corned beef; it is just not part of my diet.)

Anyway, many other things happened, and I had to go back to Montreal, to take care of business. As I was upstairs shaving, it occurred to me that Joan should write me a note to come back, and should stuff it into my bag. I came back downstairs and told her this, and she said the same thing had just occurred to her.

And it was like this throughout this whole relationship. Finally, she broke up with me, because she claimed I was too hung up. She had a choice to make between me and her uncle and aunt, and she chose them. She was more experienced than me in every respect, and I was still wet behind the ears. So I did move back to Montreal, where I majored in philosophy in third year at Loyola, but that's another story...

December 8, 2011

9. THE VALUE OF A LIBERAL EDUCATION

I haven't told this story in a long time. Every word of it is true, so help me God.

In April 1968, I was hitchhiking from Montreal to Vancouver with a teenage lady called Ann Wells, whom I had met at a party in NDG that spring. We left with a total of fifteen dollars in our pockets and one night, a car dropped us off in Cereal, which was a village of perhaps two hundred people, just on the border of Alberta and Saskatchewan. It was night time and also very dark.

We got dropped off at a crossroads. There was a gas station and a grocery store, as well as a dirt road going into town. As I said, it was night.

We stuck out our thumb and tried to hitch a ride out of there. After a few minutes, along came a beaten up old car, with six guys inside. They rolled down their windows and got a look at us. "Look, we can cut the hippie's hair," I heard one of the fellows say. They had a wild glare in their eyes, like a pack of hungry wolves that had not seen flesh in a long while.

Their faces were deformed by too much alcohol and they looked like red necks. I replied, "That's OK, we'll pass." And they drove off in their old Ford car.

We stuck out our thumbs and tried our luck again.

Another car pulled up to us, coming from town, and paused two minutes while they opened the door and threw out a woman into the ditch of the dirt road. The car drove off, and an apparition of a woman crawled out of the ditch and hobbled toward us. She said she was from Newfoundland and was native. She had just been gangraped by some brutes, who threw her afterwards into the ditch. She looked lost, her eyes rolling, and she said she was "just wandering."

At this point, Ann and I walked up to the grocery store, where some of the local people were gathered and talking. "Who are these people?" one of them asked. The man behind the counter replied, "Wanderers, who come around and make life hard for the honest folk." I don't know, we were just getting out of the cold for a minute.

We were looking out the window at the highway. Outside, the native lady was hitchhiking and we were shocked to see she got picked up by the six red necks in the Ford. She got into the car.

I figured she got gang raped a second time that night.

It was around ten o'clock at night.

That was when we met a farmer woman, who offered to let us stay at her place, overnight, if we were willing to wait for her husband. He was drinking at the local hotel. So we got into her car and waited outside the hotel, which was a miserable hovel of a place with a neon sign at the door. We waited for two hours in the dark, until midnight. Then he came out and took the driver's seat. We drove for perhaps half an hour to a farm, where they were tenant farmers. They lived in a trailer and their old Chevy car had seen better days. They told us their story: he had never been to school, but she had a grade two education. Also, he had never traveled to another town, but she had been to the next town over, which was fifteen miles away. They had a portable television in their trailer, which equipped with electricity. They let us sleep on a mattress in the back of the trailer.

In the morning, a squeaky, cranky yellowish streak of sun appeared on the horizon, and the farmer drove us back out to the highway. I noticed he had a beer as he started his car and said to it, "Chevy car, you no go this morning?" And when he finished his beer, he rolled down his window and threw the empty bottle over the roof of the car into the field on the right.

Finally, we did make it to Vancouver, after traveling through the third world. That summer I went back to university at Loyola College in Montreal. I was nineteen years old.

June 6, 2013

10. A IS NOT NOT-A

The families line up at the cash, and yes, it looks boring: the fathers are holding the little boys' hands, and the mothers are fussing, looking through their purses, and the little girls are running wild, running circles around their parents, and this is what it is all about if you have kids. Your turn arrives, and you come up to the cashier at the Biodome. He asks you how many tickets you want, and you reply: two adults and so many children. The cashier gives you your tickets, and then you go to the cloakroom, to drop off your boots and coats. Of course, the little boy has to go to the bathroom, and the little girls are fighting, and the parents are totally stressed out. But the grown-ups are learning to become patient. They will be mature some day.

I remember asking a lady of the night once, "Why are you working as a call-girl?"

And she replied, dead serious: "Because I didn't want a house in suburbia with a white picket fence, and a husband in a T-shirt, holding a can of beer in his hand."

So you pays your money and you makes your choice.

However, what is not obvious is that family living is not an option for many other people, like the homeless. Some people, like gays or clergy, as well as certain dedicated artists, choose not to reproduce, because their heart is elsewhere, but the homeless are considered not eligible to have kids.

Meanwhile, the family has begun visiting the exhibit, and look, daddy, there is a crocodile!! And where is Johnny? I don't know, he was here a minute ago. He must have run off to go see the monkeys. And mommy, Alyssa won't stop bugging me!

And there are hundreds of families in the municipal exhibit, and it can be at the Old Port, it can be the Nutcracker Suite at Christmas time, it can be the Dow Planetarium – what else can you do with your family on a Sunday afternoon? And the exhibits are crowded, and they are shovelling real money into real trucks with real shovels. And the whole bloody economy runs on this: the Sunday afternoon with the kids.

Perhaps it seems boring to outsiders, perhaps the parents are totally on edge and want to blow up at their kids; perhaps daddy has had to work all week to pay for these outings. Someone had to wash the kids' clothes, feed them, toilet-train them, take them to school, do homework with the children. Kids are not a package deal: they don't come into this world already trained and ready to go.

And there is definitely a dialectic here: the kids just want to watch videos, eat junk food, go to bed at all hours of the night, and they are the proles. Meanwhile, mom and dad want to bring up their kids, and they have an agenda for the young ones, and they are management. And the class struggle goes on. One thing, however, is for sure – having kids means instant morality.

Meanwhile, the homeless people are not part of this. They are sleeping in subway stations, on hard benches, after spending their last sixty dollars on a bag full of coke. Theirs are cheap thrills, and they are not happy. But would they want to fuss over kids, the way you do? Would they want to wake up at six o'clock every morning, to go to work and prepare breakfast for a family of four? Would they want to do homework as though school started all over again, at the age of forty? Is it a choice, a vocation like for Benedict Labre? Do the homeless have a choice?

A IS NOT NOT-A

A is not not-A. The homeless are excluded from the family exhibit. The street people, the hookers, the hustlers and panhandlers have made their choice. You can't have your cake and eat it. And trust me, there are plenty of times when the parents would gladly want to throw in the towel, and go party. Something keeps you committed. Something that looks like an angel when it is sleeping, under the blankets, with its mouth slightly open, dreaming little angel dreams.

Where are the homeless? They are not here. Their absence is conspicuous. Because families sleep at night. You might say raising children means not having adventures. You might say it fills the heart with joy.

January 11, 2004

Written with the financial assistance of the Conseil des arts et des lettres du Québec.

11. SOUL ON ICE

"The idea was that if a butterfly chances to flap his wings in Beijing in March, then, by August, hurricane patterns in the Atlantic will be completely different."
- James Gleick, *Chaos*

I was a self-styled tourist in Spain in 1967, when I was eighteen years old. After hitchhiking alone from Madrid, I found myself in a small hotel, a *pension*, in Barcelona run by a Spanish family which was friends with Marcello, the fellow who had driven me from the capital. The cost of living was extremely cheap in those days, and at night, I acted like a big boy and went drinking down by the harbour. One night, for instance, I ended up in a gay bar, where all the customers wore *toreador* costumes, with skin-tight gold pants, berets and beauty spots painted on their faces. The barmaid sold *calamara* (octopus) the way they sell peanuts in taverns here, and everyone kept chanting, *Cenga su madré* (fuck your mother). I felt perfectly at home in this wild atmosphere, but I moved on to another watering hole before some guy got the idea to try to pick me up. During the daytime, Marcello's nephew would take me around to see the sights in Barcelona, from the *Ramblas* to the government buildings where armed soldiers kept guard holding machine guns. Military parades were a frequent occurrence in that seaport, and another time, I was in a post office and saw a British tourist get her passport confiscated by the *Guardia civil* because her dress exposed her shoulders in a government location. Spain was under the iron heel of Franco. You didn't want to get into trouble, because everyone was afraid of the State police, the *Guardia civil*. As George Orwell said in *Homage to Catalonia*, Franco's governance meant power was in the hands of the military, the aristocracy and the Church. There were labour unions all right, but they ate out of the hands of bosses. You didn't say anything about communism or revolution, because you could get lynched. Despite the vibrant spirit of the Spanish people, the country was fascist and the people expressed their passionate spirit at bullfights. One night, in a bar, I watched *flamenco* dancers hammering the floor with their ardent heels, and the atmosphere was electric. The only outlet for American culture was a 1930s edition of a Flash Gordon magazine that I found among used books at a bookstore.

I stayed in Barcelona for almost a month, since the cost of the hotel was so cheap. One night, in the lobby of the hotel, the television set was on and there was a graphic report about the riots in some major city in the United States. It was summertime, and the ghettoes were each exploding, one after another, as the racial tensions built up and overflowed. Black people were fed up with their lot in the American system.

Anyway, there was a family of black American tourists staying at this hotel with me, a middle-class family with young children, and the father and I were watching the reports about the riots. Obviously, this man was not very politicized, because he exclaimed, "What are they protesting about!!?" (He was asking *me*...) I answered what I could, not really understanding either, until a few minutes later, the eight or ten year old son of the hotel owner spit in the face of the black businessman's son. A big commotion ensued, and the white hotel owners tried to apologize to these customers, in broken English.

And that is why there were riots in Harlem, and Watts, and Oakland.

June 22, 2013

12. WAITING FOR THE SNOW

"Ah, distinctly I remember, it was in the bleak December"
- Edgar Allan Poe, The Raven

Yes, December was approaching quickly, and so was rent day, the first of the month: I was broke, because work never came in during the fall. On the other hand, I was sober, and my children were doing well in college. If we were still eating every day, it was largely due to my wife. I had met Roger at the government clinic where I was treated for various ailments, and he had struck me as a nice guy. So we became buddies.

I had introduced him to my younger sister, and he was enthralled with her looks. Right away, he made a move on her, just routinely flirting with her, until she fell into his arms. Or rather, she fell into his bed, and had to take the morning-after pill because she hadn't used any protection. Within a moment of hearing about this, he abandoned her and found a new paramour. I wasn't too thrilled about this.

He had confided in me, and told me he came from a dysfunctional family in Nova Scotia. When he had moved to Montreal, he went wild, discovering all the nightlife, glitter, and glamour, and finally – the sleaze. Being a poet, he felt it was his birthright to sleep with every skirt he met, to experiment with every substance available, and to stop taking care of himself. You might say he was a lost little boy of twenty-seven going on seventeen.

I heard the sound OM that fall, at a time when I was as unstable as in 1968, when I first heard it. According to the Upanishads, it is the sound of the Universe. I was sitting in my living room, dirty, unshaven, dishevelled, and yet saying my rosary, when it happened. The room was filled with a Presence, and I could distinctly hear the sound. My girlfriend/mother of my children entered the room and asked me why I looked so funny. She was not part of this mystical experience, but I just laughed. I immediately connected with the first time I had heard the OM, tripping on acid, in the days when I worked as a street pharmacist, when I used to permanently borrow toilet paper from restaurants and stuff it under my coat, when the police followed me around, not really to get my autograph. And here I was, forty-three years later, in 2011, sober, the father of two kids, and a professional translator.

Roger and I still were friends, because I still felt like a street person, and although he had a part-time job, he had one foot in the gutter and the other on a banana peel. I wanted to save this poor soul. I felt it was my missionary duty to rescue him and take him under my wing. But he was stronger than me, driven by a passion for poetry that was totally magnetic. I didn't know if I wanted to indulge with him or convert him. (God forbid I should convert anyone…)

Anyhow, this is where we stood, at the end of November 2011, when I was still able to work, when he was still a star of the poetry establishment. But what ensued could not be predicted.

The leaves had fallen and lay strewn about in the brown/gray gutters of Montreal; the trees were skeletal and bare, like big spider legs clutching at the cloudy November sky. Roger and I were blown about by a devastating wind that would wreak havoc in our lives and those of others.

You have heard of Neil Cassidy and Jack Kerouac –

well, I am not exactly Kerouac, but Roger was every bit as much of a psychopath as Cassidy. Push came to shove: he tried to get me published, I tried to get him published, and naught came of it. So we decided to go on a rampage together. I permanently borrowed my wife's credit card, and we made reservations for a one-way flight to Vancouver, he a twenty-seven year old maniac, and I a sixty-three year old fool who should know better. And sure enough, how we ended up at Main & Hastings, panhandling, is a sad story, full of sound and fury, signifying nothing, but it was a matter of time before – in mid-December – he hooked up with some junkies and began stealing, while I was phoning my wife and kids collect, trying to backtrack and make overdue amends. I had run up a debt on my wife's credit card, and credit had expired.

Finally, I don't know what happened to Roger, because we parted ways when he began to shoot drugs. I contacted a rich friend of mine in Montreal who was vice-President at Bombardier; he sent me money for plane fare back to Montreal, and when I arrived back home, my wife had me committed to this psych ward, where I am writing this sad tale right now. I hope Roger is all right, but first, I have to impress upon the social workers that I will make it up to my wife and kids.

And I promise to never, never steal my wife's credit card again. I am laughing as I am writing this, and I don't even know why.

November 27, 2011

13. LA CHRONIQUE DU MAYA

I. BOULEVARD SAINT-LAURENT

C'est là que tout avait commencé, au coin de Saint-Laurent et de Sainte-Catherine, en face de la station de métro. J'attendais l'autobus 55 ce jour-là, lorsqu'un forcené s'est mis à crier à tue-tête en passant d'une personne à l'autre. Il avait l'air d'un sans-abri qui en voulait aux gens. Tout le monde qui attendait l'autobus au cours de cette journée d'automne 1983 faisait de son mieux pour ne pas prêter attention à la personne malade, qui ne cessait de crier des choses absurdes aux passants. Il faisait un soleil de plomb cet après-midi-là, et tout semblait en ordre. Sauf que les gens semblaient écrasés par la peur.

La personne devant moi dans la longue ligne de passagers pour prendre l'autobus 55 se retourna vers moi et me dit dans un accent que je ne reconnaissais pas, en anglais : Cet homme qui crie comme ça n'est pas forcément méchant, il est tout simplement malade.

- Oui, je lui répondis, il a un désordre au cerveau.
- Ces personnes doivent recevoir des soins.

Puis j'ai entamé une conversation avec le monsieur qui m'avait adressé la parole. Il était de ma taille, environ cinq pieds six, portait les cheveux courts et une moustache

THE WEIGHT OF ILLUSIONS

taillée. Il avait les cheveux noirs et les yeux noirs. Enfin, l'autobus est arrivé, et nous avons fait quelques coins ensemble. Il m'a raconté qu'il était Persan et venait d'immigrer au pays. Il suivait des cours de français, mais il se débrouillait assez bien en anglais pour pouvoir jaser. Je suis descendu au coin de Napoléon et je suis rentré chez moi. Je ne savais pas où il habitait.

Je ne l'ai pas revu pendant environ deux semaines. Moi, j'habitais sur la rue Coloniale, dans une espèce de taudis infesté de souris, mais j'étais tout près de quelques amis. J'avais déménagé dans un deuxième étage à partir de mon logement à Ottawa. Je venais de travailler pendant dix-neuf mois à la section de la statistique du Secrétariat d'État. J'étais un traducteur novice, et à Ottawa j'avais le mal du pays, même si je venais de la capitale. Mes racines étaient à Montréal. Alors, dès que mon emploi s'est terminé à Ottawa, je suis revenu à Montréal, sans avoir de plans précis ni espérer trouver de l'ouvrage. Je recevais de l'assurance-chômage et j'avais l'intention d'écrire un livre de poésie. J'étais tout simplement soulagé de ne plus travailler dans un bureau.

Environ deux semaines plus tard, j'ai croisé mon nouvel ami parmi les passants de la rue Prince-Arthur. Il promenait ses enfants, deux jeunes filles d'à peu près cinq ans et trois ans. Les gens mangeaient sur la terrasse des restaurants hauts-de-gamme, et lui faisait une marche avec ses petites. Tout de suite, il m'a reconnu et nous avons échangé nos coordonnées. Il s'avérait qu'il avait un logement dans un immeuble sur la rue Saint-Urbain et il avait le statut de réfugié au Canada. Son neveu venait souvent chez eux; lui s'était évadé de l'Iran afin de ne pas être conscrit dans l'armée iranienne. Et l'homme que j'avais rencontré deux semaines auparavant s'appelait Ali Mossad. Il était lui aussi poète et il avait enseigné la bibliothéconomie à l'Université de Tehran.

Ce dimanche après-midi-là, nous nous sommes promené un peu en jasant et en jouissant de la belle journée ensoleillée. Les gens autour de nous étaient insouciants et dégustaient des mets dispendieux au soleil. Il y avait plein de restaurants sur la rue Prince-Arthur, et Ali et moi, nous nous sommes perdus dans un rêve en parlant de poésie et de nos antécédents.

Moi, je ne connaissais pas grand'chose de la situation en Iran. À cette époque il y avait la guerre, mais je ne lisais pas les journaux. J'avais vu des manchettes au cours des années précédant notre rencontre. Je vivais à l'ombre, comme dans la caverne de Platon, tandis que l'ombre des événements mondiaux dansait sur les murs. Il y avait eu des manchettes au sujet des «boat people» vietnamiens, ces gens qui avaient été lancés à la mer au Vietnam, des centaines et des milliers de réfugiés qui arrivaient en Amérique du Nord. C'était en 1979, et à l'époque j'avais fait de la traduction bénévole par rapport à ces réfugiés. Tout le monde en parlait, les journaux ne parlaient que de ça, et j'avais même rencontré un jeune séminariste nommé Dominique Hong qui était lui aussi un des ces «boat people». Après quelques semaines, je crois qu'il était parti pour les États-Unis.

Mais tout à coup, les «boat people» n'existaient plus. Pouf! Vaporisés! Ce qui occupait les manchettes dans la caverne de Platon, c'était soudain les 50 otages américains dans l'ambassade américaine à Tehran. Et la caméra du monde entier se retournait vers l'Iran et la révolution étudiante qui y avait lieu. J'avais vu des manifestants iraniens bizarres au carré Philippe, qui revendiquaient l'abdication du Shah d'Iran, mais j'étais pris au dépourvu. Qui était ce Shah? Je ne savais même pas tout à fait où se trouvait l'Iran sur la carte du monde. On n'entendait plus rien au sujet des «boat people» et tout ce qui faisait du bruit, c'était la révolution persane. J'entendais des grondements à l'horizon, la nuit, je voyais des éclairs et des feux d'artifices causés par les bombes qui allaient tomber sur nous tous. Dans mes rêves, éveillés et en plein sommeil, il y avait les 50 otages coincés dans l'ambassade à Tehran. Et tous les phares semblaient braqués sur ce petit coin du monde qui faisait tant de tapage dans les médias.

Entre-temps, au Québec, le Parti Québécois avait été élu, et on attendait un référendum sur l'indépendance de la province. J'en parlais au facteur, j'en parlais à des amies qui étaient des fondamentalistes pentecôtistes, j'en parlais à ma famille, mais tout ce que je voyais des nouvelles, c'étaient les manchettes; de temps à autre, j'apercevais la tête de René Lévesque à la télé, et je saisissais des bribes par-ci par-là de ce qui se brassait dans mon propre pays. Les anglophones redoutaient René; les francophones l'adoraient. J'avais lu un livre qu'il avait écrit sur la souveraineté-association, et je ne comprenais pas plus. Où est-ce que le Québec se situait par rapport aux autres mouvements vers l'indépendance dans le monde? Notre province comptait-elle à l'échelle mondiale? Voisine des États comme elle l'était, pouvait-elle se séparer? Personne ne savait si nous pouvions survivre indépendants. C'était ça, l'enjeu...

Entre-temps, je savais bien peu de choses en 1983, quatre ans plus tard, au sujet de l'Iran. Est-ce que je le savais, moi, que les États-Unis avaient encouragé Saddam Houssein à envahir l'Iran afin d'étouffer le nouveau régime de l'ayatollah Kohmeini? On n'en parlait plus en 1983. Une autre ombre dansait sur les murs de la caverne de Platon. Puis une autre, puis une autre, afin de distraire ces masses qui s'ennuyaient. Entre-temps, je rencontrais des réfugiés, comme Dominique Hong, comme Ali Mossad, et j'entendais des bribes sur la révolution, sur la persécution, sur les mouvements de masse, et tout cela se fondait dans le bruit de ma petite tête, sur le fond de toile d'un monde en pleine explosion, et j'essayais d'abord de survivre puis de comprendre quelle lumière surgissait à l'horizon. J'allais bientôt en savoir davantage, au fur et à mesure que je rencontrais des gens qui avaient, eux, vécu de vraies aventures. Ali et sa famille allaient m'instruire. Et j'entrevoyais une lueur de liberté du côté de la porte de la caverne, et je voulais en savoir davantage sur ce monde en ébullition. Mes parents avaient toujours accueilli des immigrants chez eux, et moi je faisais pareil. Heureux qui, comme Ulysse, a fait un beau voyage, et rentre au pays en racontant les merveilles qu'il a vues à l'étranger. Moi, j'habitais près des feux clignotants de la rue Saint-Laurent, près des bars portugais merveilleux, près de tous ces nouveaux arrivants et ces bohémiens qui se côtoyaient dans un monde d'illusions. Moi, j'étais perdu, comme une feuille tombée d'un arbre pour arriver sur les flots d'un cours d'eau qui l'emporte vers l'océan. J'étais balloté par les vagues, sans agenda, sans plan de vie, et je regardais passer le paysage, les arbres, les prés, les montagnes, qui allaient en sens inverse tandis que je flottais vers la mer.

II. L'AMI PHILOSOPHE

Au cours des mois qui suivirent, j'en suis venu à connaître davantage le nouvel ami Ali. C'était un homme sérieux, un homme qui avait beaucoup souffert. Son père était membre du Parti communiste, son grand-père aussi. Quand Ali était jeune, sous le règne du Shah, son père avait passé trois ans en prison, et il était devenu musulman pendant sa captivité. Alors Ali avait été élevé coincé dans un appartement d'une seule pièce en compagnie de sa famille de onze membres. Néanmoins, il avait réussi à obtenir une maîtrise en bibliothéconomie et à enseigner cette science à l'université. Il m'avait affirmé que dans son pays d'origine, il se trouvait au sommet de l'échelle salariale. Mais une fois arrivé au Québec, il devait apprendre le français tout en étant, avec sa famille, assisté social. C'était une période heureuse pour lui, il vivait comme un bohémien et n'était pas inquiet de quoi que ce soit.

Cependant, il me raconta comment et pourquoi il avait émigré au Canada. En Iran, il était impliqué dans un mouvement révolutionnaire visant à renverser l'ayatollah Kohmeini. Au début, aux dires de son épouse Sara, pendant la révolution iranienne, c'était la partie de plaisir. S'il y avait une collision entre deux autos, les chauffeurs se donnaient des accolades. Tout le monde était en délire, selon elle, et la vie prenait un nouveau sens, une fois que le

77

Shah avait quitté le pays pour aller s'exiler aux États-Unis. Ce que me disaient Ali et Sara, ce n'est pas du tout ce que l'on entendait dans les médias. Les images qui dansaient à l'écran, dans la caverne de Platon, représentaient des étudiants barbus qui brûlaient l'image de Jimmy Carter en effigie. Personne dans l'Occident n'était prêt pour la révolution iranienne. On parlait d'envoyer le Cid de Corneille en Iran pour libérer les 50 otages américains. Il y avait même eu une mission américaine pour les libérer, et l'hélicoptère s'était écrasé – c'était un fiasco. Les Américains, qui étaient si puissants, avec leur bombe atomique, étaient réduits à l'impuissance.

Mais l'histoire ne se termine pas là. Mon nouvel ami Ali était un leader du mouvement pour renverser l'ayatollah, qui se mettait à imposer un régime musulman fondamentaliste comme on n'en avait pas vu depuis le Moyen-Âge. Ali s'était évadé de son pays en passant par les montagnes de la Turquie, parce que sa vie était en danger. Ses camarades se faisaient torturer par la police de l'ayatollah, qui voulait savoir où était disparu, où était rendu Ali. Celui-ci m'avait donné des détails. La police prenait une hache pour trancher une jambe aux révolutionnaires, pour les faire parler. «Où est rendu Ali?» Alors mon nouvel ami venait de sortir de l'enfer, comme Orphée, et parlait beaucoup de la souffrance. Il n'avait pas le coeur gai. Nous nous promenions ensemble dans le plateau Mont-Royal, en discutant du sens de la vie, tandis qu'autour de nous, autour de Krisna et Arjuna, il y avait un champ de bataille sanglant. Nous passions en char à travers cette hécatombe, et tout semblait une illusion, le maya, comme le dit si bien la Bahgavad-Gita.

Évidemment, la consolation d'Ali, c'étaient ses deux enfants et sa belle épouse Sara. Elle était ingénieur agricole dans son pays, mais au Canada, elle ne pouvait pas pratiquer son métier. Son diplôme n'était pas reconnu. Lui, Ali, ne pouvait pas être bibliothécaire, sans suivre des cours d'informatique afin de parfaire son éducation. Alors les deux vivaient de l'assistance sociale. Et elle laissait parler Ali.

Lui et moi entretenions des conversations philosophiques au cours de la soirée, quand j'allais casser la croûte chez eux, en compagnie de leurs enfants. Nous pouvions comparer nos deux religions. Lui connaissait l'Islam et moi, la chrétienté. Par exemple, Ali m'avait raconté que Mahomet avait traversé le désert sur un cheval blanc. Puis, il était monté aux cieux sur le cheval, et en était redescendu pour fonder la religion musulmane. Et moi, je me disais : «Voyons, les chevaux ne volent pas dans les airs... Mais alors que faire de l'ascension de Jésus? Si le cheval de Mahomet, c'était du mythe, alors est-ce que l'ascension de Jésus ne relèverait-elle pas aussi de la mythologie?» Et les conversations de Krisna et d'Arjuna, en premier plan, contre l'arrière-plan des événements mondiaux, comme la guerre entre l'Irak et l'Iran, alimentée par l'oncle Sam, rendaient transparentes les machinations politiques, la mystification religieuse, la propagande dont on nourrissait les masses et dans l'Occident et dans le monde arabe. Il y avait beaucoup de supercherie dans l'air. Ali et moi étions décidés d'en venir à bout. Le chariot d'Arjuna passait à travers le champ de bataille, et on entendait les téléviseurs citer à tort et à travers les propos des leaders musulmans, qu'on traduisait faussement pour tromper les masses.

Ali était futé en politique. Lors d'un sommet entre Gorbatchev et Reagan, Ali m'avait dit, très cynique, que si les deux leaders s'entendaient, c'était pour fourrer les peuples du monde; s'ils ne s'entendaient pas, c'était la guerre nucléaire. Alors il n'y avait pas grand espoir dans le monde d'Ali! Il me parlait de l'ange exterminateur, dont on parle dans l'Islam. Et cet ange était très occupé, surtout en temps de guerre! Mais mon nouvel ami, qui était pince-sans-rire, ne s'esclaffait jamais de ses boutades. Il disait tout sur un ton sérieux. Ses sourcils noirs et épais étaient toujours froncés.

Son épouse était plus humaine. J'essayais de lui expliquer ce qu'était la miséricorde, même si elle ne parlait pas beaucoup français ou anglais. Je lui disais que la miséricorde consistait à traiter ses enfants avec gentillesse et respect, même s'ils faisaient des mauvais coups. À un moment donné, j'avais commencé à lire le Coran, l'Écriture sainte des musulmans, et j'avais dit à Sara que si j'ouvrais le livre au hasard, je ne tombais pas sur un oracle, sur un verset qui me concernait. Et Sara de répondre : c'est parce que tu n'y crois pas. Et j'avais demandé à Ali pourquoi, dans les premiers chapitres du Coran, on répétait sans cesse : «Le massacre vaut mieux que l'oppression.» Ali m'avait fait remarquer que ce verset devait être interprété.

Pour le reste, c'était une famille normale. Un père. Une mère. Deux enfants. Les enfants étaient espiègles, la mère changeait des couches, le père aussi, et ils s'inquiétaient tous les deux du sort que leur réservait l'avenir. Ils arrivaient toujours à joindre les deux bouts, après bien des sacrifices. Ils ne faisaient pas la grosse vie, mais à cette époque, ils n'avaient pas de tracas.

J'en suis venu à comprendre toutefois que ces gens avaient des valeurs légèrement différentes des nôtres. Un soir, par exemple, j'avais été invité à une soirée en famille chez eux. Le frère de Sara était présent et il y avait plusieurs personnes. Eux racontaient des histoires de torture, d'opium, de prison, de mitraillettes, de violence, bref des choses dont on ne parle pas en société parmi les gens d'ici. J'avais demandé à Ali s'il y avait quelque chose que je pourrais faire pour aider leur cause et lui m'avait répondu en me demandant si je savais comment utiliser une mitraillette? Enfin, cette discussion saugrenue en famille s'était poursuivie au cours de la soirée, et pour faire changement, j'avais conté une farce sexuelle, de mauvais goût. Tout de suite, on m'a mis à la porte. Ce que j'avais dit était considéré inapproprié. Eux pouvaient parler de révolution en famille, mais la moindre allusion sexuelle ne passait pas. (J'avais appris une leçon...)

Néanmoins, l'ami Ali avait acquis un grand respect pour moi et pour mes parents. Une fois, le frère d'Ali s'était évadé de l'Iran et s'était retrouvé sans un sou à Istanbul. Alors j'avais demandé à mon père de l'aider. Mon père était membre de l'Ordre de Jacques Cartier, et la charité, c'était son fort. Et mon père avait envoyé cent cinquante dollars par Western Union au frère d'Ali à Istanbul, même s'il n'avait jamais rencontré ni Ali ni son frère. Ali était demeuré reconnaissant envers mon père pendant bien des années à suivre, parce que papa l'avait dépanné. Quand jamais mes parents venaient en visite à Montréal, Ali faisait en sorte que ses deux filles prennent un bain, s'habillent comme il faut et viennent rencontrer mes parents. Et mon père trouvait qu'Ali avait quelque chose de spécial, que c'était un gentilhomme.

J'ai perdu de vue Ali et sa famille temporairement pendant cet hiver-là, parce que j'ai eu des problèmes de santé d'ordre neurologique. Entre-temps, les ombres dansaient sur les parois de la caverne de Platon, sauf que je ne pouvais plus interpréter correctement les signes que mes cinq sens transmettaient à mon cerveau. Je passais beaucoup de temps dans les rues de Montréal et une fois, un ami anglophone à moi voulait dire que j'avais l'air bronzé et m'avait dit que j'avais l'air d'un Libanais avec une mission. J'avais les yeux grand ouverts et j'avais l'air dangereux. J'étais devenu un fantôme qui dansait sur les murs!

III. LE PACIFISTE

Entre-temps, comme dans Les Lettres à un supérieur provincial de Pascal, je passais en catamini d'un ami philosophe à l'autre, afin de me renseigner. Une personne que je trouvais intéressante, à l'époque, était mon ami Rusty, dont le vrai prénom était Arnold et dont le prénom juif était Aaron. Il enseignait un cours sur le poète anglais William Blake au Collège Vanier, à Ville Saint-Laurent. Il faisait partie du mouvement pacifiste mondial et nous avions de longues discussions sur la politique et la religion comparée. En 1983, je venais de terminer des études en traduction à l'Université de Montréal, et lui suivait un cours de linguistique sur Noam Chomsky, car il voulait enseigner l'anglais comme langue seconde. Et il m'expliquait que l'objectif du mouvement pacifiste, c'était que Gorbatchev et Reagan se parlent, au moins, au lieu de faire peser sur l'humanité le spectre de la guerre nucléaire, et qu'ils entreprennent la réduction des stocks de bombes atomiques. Ces deux leaders étaient des ombres qui dansaient sur la paroi de la caverne de Platon, et moi, je ne voyais pas comment des gens ordinaires pouvaient exercer une influence quelconque sur des figures médiatiques d'un tel ordre. Le monde entier frissonnait pendant la Guerre froide et la lueur d'espoir à la bouche de la caverne, c'était un nouveau dialogue, une nouvelle dialectique entre les super-puissances qui s'affrontaient. Pendant que le leader soviétique et le président américain discutaient dans le cadre de leurs sommets, il y avait un champ de bataille autour d'eux, comme autour du char de Krisna et d'Arjuna. L'enjeu semblait énorme : la survie de l'humanité, et Rusty me faisait comprendre que, s'il y avait une guerre nucléaire, aucune vie ne serait possible par après pendant la durée de vie du plutonium, c'est-à-dire 99 000 années de notre calendrier.

Au début, je ne me rendais pas compte combien la situation était grave. Non pas que je prenais les choses à la légère, mais je fréquentais aussi des évangélistes chrétiens, qui brandissaient la menace de la fin du monde. Et on m'avait déjà fait le coup de la fin du monde, en mai 1960, quand les bonnes sœurs avaient annoncé aux enfants d'école francophones catholiques que c'était la fin du monde et ce, de Winnipeg à Fredericton, en passant par Ottawa, Québec et Montréal. Le 1er mai de cette année-là, toute l'école avait passé la journée à l'église, en attendant les bombes, ou les anges, ou la terreur. Je priais tous les soirs que les Russes ne nous attaquent pas pendant la nuit à grands coups de bombes atomiques. Alors, vingt ans plus tard, je savais ce qu'était la bombe atomique. Je tiens juste à mentionner que le lendemain, le 2 mai, les sœurs étaient couvertes de ridicule. Et bien des jeunes ont perdu la foi de leurs parents. C'est ce qu'Ali disait, que notre génération avait perdu la foi, c'est aussi ce que pensaient Rusty et mes amis et amies. Ce qui était dur à comprendre, c'était pourquoi en une époque où tous étaient éduqués, où la science était à la veille de découvrir la base de la vie génétique, il y aurait un mouvement intégriste aux États-Unis, en Iran et parmi les hassidim. C'était une tendance rétrograde, absurde, qui allait à l'encontre du bon sens.

Rusty et moi nous allions nous étendre sur les prés du parc Jeanne-Mance, au bord du Mont-Royal, et lui étudiait Chomsky et moi j'écrivais de la poésie. Puis il m'expliquait que Chomsky prouvait presque qu'il y a une nature humaine universelle, puisqu'il retrouvait les mêmes syllabes dans les balbutiements des bébés de toutes les cultures du monde. Puis il m'expliquait pourquoi il ne croyait pas à la naissance miraculeuse de Jésus. De mon côté, j'avais téléphoné au Congrès juif canadien et j'avais demandé de parler à un érudit en langue hébreu. Je lui avais demandé : «Dans Ésaïe chapitre 9, l'Ancien Testament prédit que Dieu donnera un signe : une vierge ou une jeune femme donnera naissance à un enfant, qu'elle nommera Emmanuel.» Ensuite, j'ai demandé au vieux monsieur à l'autre bout de la ligne si, en hébreu, on parlait d'une vierge ou d'une jeune fille. Lui de me répondre : «Le mot hébreu en question est *alba*, qui se traduit soit par vierge, soit par jeune fille. Les deux traductions sont bonnes. Les chrétiens croient qu'il s'agit d'une vierge, et les Juifs croient qu'il s'agit d'une jeune femme. Vous êtes sur la bonne voie.» Et la lumière fut. Je commençais à comprendre, mais Rusty s'impatientait avec moi, parce que je croyais à des idées chrétiennes. Un soir, il m'avait emmené voir *Le Chagrin et la pitié*. Il voulait m'éduquer. Cependant, Simon Weil avait dit au sujet de ce film qu'il n'était pas réaliste, que l'Occupation en 1940 n'avait rien à foutre avec ce qui est dépeint dans ce film. Je ne sais pas. Autant de fantômes qui dansaient sur les parois de la caverne de Platon. Je n'étais pas là en 1940. Je n'étais même pas au monde encore. Mais les Juifs depuis l'holocauste répètent les mêmes histoires, de persécution, de tueries, d'antisémitisme, et ce fardeau est lourd sur leurs épaules. Rusty, lui, croyait que les pays démocratiques étaient la lumière du monde et avaient la mission d'éclairer, d'apporter la paix dans le monde, de faire briller le flambeau de la liberté. (Il faut mentionner qu'il était américain. Il avait émigré au Canada.)

Je tirais certainement une leçon de courage des amis de mes parents qui étaient Juifs et qui avaient survécu à l'holocauste. Une amie de ma mère me disait que pendant l'Occupation, en France, dix pour cent des gens étaient des héros, dans la Résistance; dix pour cent étaient des salauds, des collaborateurs, mais la grosse majorité des gens essayaient juste de survivre, du jour au lendemain. Elle ne faisait pas de cas du fait qu'elle avait été internée en camp de concentration, et son mari aussi.

Mais il ne fallait pas parler de la question palestinienne à mes amis juifs. Certains d'entre eux voyaient rouge si on disait le moindre mal au sujet d'Israël. Mon ami Pierre surtout, coupait les liens avec moi à tout bout de champ s'il soupçonnait quoi que ce soit d'antisémite. J'avais lu le Testament d'un poète assassiné, d'Élie Weisel; j'avais lu Au nom des miens, de Martin Gray – je savais un peu ce qu'avaient enduré les Juifs au cours de l'histoire de l'Europe. Elie Weisel décrivait un progrom : la veille de Noël, les chrétiens en Russie arrivaient dans les villages juifs, mettaient les maisons des gens en feu, violaient les femmes juives et gravaient des croix avec un couteau sur le visage des bébés. Martin Gray décrivait le massacre des Juifs dans le ghetto de Varsovie, les gens lapidés et tués à coup de pelle. Alors, les survivants de l'holocauste et leurs enfants n'avaient aucune sympathie pour les terroristes palestiniens qui s'en prenaient aux Juifs. Comme dans la caverne de Platon, j'avais vu à la télé le reportage sur le massacre des athlètes juifs aux Jeux olympiques vers la fin des années 70. Plus tard, j'allais voir la démolition des deux tours à New York, lors des attaques terroristes du 11 septembre 2001. Je n'oublierai jamais l'image sur le petit écran des gens qui fuyaient les immeubles en démolition. Non, le terrorisme n'est pas la solution. Il n'y a pas d'excuse pour justifier le meurtre insensé des innocents. Cela fait juste abattre les foudres de la répression des dieux sur tout le monde. L'Amérique avait mal réagi aux attaques du 11 septembre. Elle avait envahi l'Irak, sous prétexte que Saddam avait des armes nucléaires. Et pourtant, les inspecteurs de l'ONU n'avaient pas trouvé l'ombre d'une trace des armes nucléaires recherchées. Le fait est que George W. Bush convoitait le pétrole de l'Irak. Et le mensonge et la désinformation, la propagande, les supercheries avaient justifié l'invasion de l'Irak. C'était le maya dont parle la Bhavagad-Gita, l'illusion.

Alors je passais du temps avec Rusty, nous discutions, et moi d'écrire de la poésie, et lui avait composé une pièce de théâtre. Il étudiait la linguistique et connaissait la philosophie médiévale. Un soir, il m'avait expliqué la preuve de l'existence de Dieu de dom Scot. Il s'agissait d'un faux raisonnement et moi, je lui avais expliqué ce qu'était une scotomisation - le fait qu'une personne croit à une idéologie sans se rendre compte pourquoi. Par exemple, une femme qui, enfant, aurait été abusée par son père, pourrait devenir féministe, une fois adulte, mais ne serait pas consciente de la raison pour laquelle elle croit au féminisme. Et Krisna et Arjuna discutaient de la nature de la réalité, tandis que les gens s'entretuent au nom des principes et des langues et des religions, pour le bénéfice des hommes d'affaires.

Lui, Rusty, insistait que le mérite des Juifs était qu'ils avaient été les premiers monothéistes, même si lui-même était moniste et bouddhiste. Il avait fait plusieurs voyages en Inde et avait passé des semaines dans la retraite du Dalaï Lama. Comme bien des Occidentaux qui ne peuvent pas composer avec les religions officielles de l'Occident, il se prenait pour un disciple de Gautama Bouddha. Ce qui clochait, c'était la consommation d'alcool et de drogue, c'était le mode de vie occidental, c'était toute la façon de voir les choses d'un citoyen américain. Il avait beau passer pour illuminé, mais il croyait au fond que l'Amérique était supérieure au reste du monde. Il parlait seulement une langue, l'anglais, et avait été élevé en face d'un téléviseur.

Moi, j'écoutais, j'apprenais, à tort et à travers, selon l'influence des gens qui m'entouraient. Je n'avais jamais voyagé au Moyen-Orient, mais Rusty y était déjà allé. Il trouvait que les Israélites en Israël n'avaient pas le temps d'être polis, ne trouvaient pas le temps pour dire merci et s'il-vous-plaît. Ils étaient endurcis par leur mode de vie. Ils étaient existentialistes, parce qu'il y avait toujours une attaque terroriste qui les attendait d'une minute à l'autre. Selon lui, Israël était entourée de pays hostiles qui voulaient l'enfouir dans la mer. Lui ne parlait pas de la répression des Palestiniens, il comprenait juste la situation des Juifs.

Pourtant Rusty n'était pas Zioniste. Il ne croyait pas à la Bible et aux prophéties qui promettaient la terre promise aux descendants juifs d'Abraham. Il était moniste et essayait de comprendre la réalité. Il m'avait dit que relativement au Québec, il était indépendantiste. Mais il savait fort bien que si le Québec devenait indépendant, les minorités souffriraient. C'était un prix qu'il fallait payer.

Nous discutions, et nous discutions, et comme dit Gurdjieff, c'était des aliments pour la lune. Tout notre mélodrame humain, toutes nos aventures et nos mésaventures – des aliments pour la lune. Du maya, de l'illusion, qui cachait la Réalité suprême de Brahman, de Dieu.

IV. LA RÉVOLUTION ARABE

Mon premier contact avec le monde arabe proprement dit a eu lieu à Paris en 1967. J'avais alors dix-huit ans et je voyageais en Europe de l'Ouest tout seul, sur le pouce, en train, et j'avais rencontré un noir de Guadeloupe qui parlait français avec moi. Il me faisait voir Paris la nuit. Il m'avait présenté à un ami allemand à lui qui faisait de la peinture abstraite. Puis il m'avait emmené dans un café, enfoui dans un sous-sol, que fréquentaient des Algériens. Or, je portais la barbe et les cheveux longs, ainsi qu'une veste militaire américaine. Je me prenais pour un trafiquant de drogue, à l'époque, et je ne savais pas ce qui se brassait dans le monde autour de moi. À Paris, j'avais vu des manchettes dans les kiosques de journaux qui criaient des nouvelles sensationnelles au sujet des hippies. Je ne connaissais pas. «Hippie? Connais pas...» Et pourtant, à Londres, j'étais allé à Piccadilly Circus, j'avais vu les boutiques de vêtements psychédéliques, j'avais vu les jeunes qui jouaient de la guitare dans la rue, et pourtant, je n'étais pas branché au mouvement hippie. Les Algériens dans le café à Paris, eux, ils reconnaissaient que je portais un uniforme militaire et assis le long des murs à boire leur café, ils me faisaient des gros yeux. Ils avaient l'air hostiles, et moi, je le sentais, que je n'étais pas le bienvenu. Il s'était fait un silence autour de moi, dès que j'étais rentré dans la place. Alors mon ami de Guadeloupe m'avait pris par le bras et m'avait fait sortir de ce café avant qu'il n'y ait du trouble.

Pourtant, je ne lisais jamais les journaux. Je ne savais pas qu'il y avait eu une révolution en Algérie. Je n'avais pas entendu parler des bombes à Paris. Je n'avais jamais entendu scander le slogan «d'Algérie aux Algériens!» Dans ce café à Paris, je me trouvais vraiment en milieu underground. Je ne le savais pas. Plus tard, à l'université, j'avais eu un prof de science politique qui avait fait la révolution en Algérie. Il nous avait raconté que la police française en Algérie plantait une bombe dans un cinéma plein d'enfants, puis elle publiait un communiqué affirmant que les révolutionnaires avaient commis ce coup pendable. Autant d'ombres sur les parois de la caverne de Platon. Ensuite, la population chassait les révolutionnaires, croyant que les coupables, c'étaient eux. Et Franz Fanon décrit qu'un révolutionnaire algérien qui avait été torturé par la police française pouvait se trouver dans un poste de police en Algérie pendant la révolution, et apercevoir un policier français de loin; tout de suite, de son propre chef, le révolutionnaire en psychose courait jusqu'aux toilettes et se plantait lui-même la tête dans le bol! Fanon était psychiâtre et traitait des cas semblables pendant la guerre en Algérie.

Eux, les Algériens dans le café qui me faisaient de gros yeux, est-ce qu'ils savaient ce qu'était la révolution culturelle, qui étaient les Beatles et le mouvement psychédélique? Pour un révolutionnaire, le mouvement hippie devait paraître farfelu... Et moi, non plus, je n'en avais à peu près pas entendu parler. En rentrant au Canada, je m'étais aperçu que tous mes amis parlaient du LSD25 et de l'album des Beatles *Sergeant Pepper*. Comme l'aurait dit mon ami Ali Mossad, c'était une mode, comme le mouvement punk. Pourtant, tout le monde embarquait. Il y avait des naïfs comme moi, qui croyaient trouver l'illumination en prenant une tablette d'acide; il y avait des croches, qui vendaient de la drogue et des houkas. Il y avait beaucoup de commerçants, qui ouvraient des boutiques de musique psychédélique et d'affiches délirantes. Et tout cela, semble-t-il, avec la bénédiction du gouvernement. «On va tous les rendre fous. Comme ça, ils nous foutront la paix.» Entre-temps, des compagnies canadiennes fabriquaient du LSD pour la Central Intelligence Agency, qui tentait des expériences sur les prisonniers Viet Cong. On donnait du LSD à un Viet Cong puis on le torturait, pour le faire parler. Des compagnies canadiennes comme Sandoz, qui fabriquait de l'acide pur. D'autres compagnies canadiennes produisaient du napalm, pour l'armée américaine, qui était impliquée au Viet Nam. Évidemment, on sait que si du napalm touche à votre bras, il brûle jusqu'à ce qu'il ne reste plus rien, sauf des cendres. Et les soldats américains projetaient du napalm sur les Viet Cong et puis les regardaient brûler... Quand j'étais à l'université, à Montréal, j'avais assisté à des rallyes pacifistes à l'Université McGill, où l'on nous faisait voir des films vidéo de soldats américains qui riaient de leurs victimes en feu. Aussi, au Collège Loyola, un soir, par hasard, j'avais assisté à un long métrage intitulé *Meinkampf*, un documentaire objectif au sujet des atrocités de l'holocauste, pendant la Deuxième Guerre mondiale. Je pensais voir un film d'horreur à la Hitchcock, mais non, il s'agissait de vraies atrocités, commises envers des vrais Juifs! J'étais estomaqué, car pendant toute mon éducation au primaire et au secondaire, on ne m'avait jamais parlé de l'holocauste. Enfin, le lessivage de cerveau consiste à constamment répéter le même message aux gens et à tenir une partie de la réalité à l'ombre. Tout ça pour dire que lorsque Krisna et le roi Arjuna déambulaient dans le champ de bataille, dans la Bhagavad-Gita, ça commençait à puer l'être humain. Autant j'avais lu Saint-Exupéry et ses récits au sujet de la grandeur humaine, autant la terre des hommes me semblait polluée, autant le diable avait une emprise sur le cerveau de certaines gens.

Quand j'étais à Paris, je ne croyais ni à dieu ni à diable ni à mon père, comme dirait Félix. J'étais un fils révolté – contre quoi? Contre l'Église et la duplicité de mes parents qui m'avaient imposé deux ans de petit séminaire. Mais à un autre niveau, j'étais encore bien naïf. J'avais beau lire Karl Marx et Jean-Paul Sartre, mais qu'est-ce que je comprenais? Pas plus que les masses qui regardent, les yeux écarquillés, les ombres qui dansent sur les parois de la caverne de Platon.

D'ailleurs, l'ignorance est le pire ennemi. Lorsque j'ai rencontré mon ami Ali Mossad de nouveau, lui et sa famille avaient passé un séjour d'un an à Longueuil, sur la rive Sud. Il m'a dit que pendant une année entière, son voisin du même palier, du même étage, ne lui avait jamais même dit bonjour. Tu parles d'une façon de se débarrasser des immigrants! On s'assure ainsi que le quartier restera monochrome! Ma conjointe et moi avions essayé une fois de louer un appartement à Westmount, et la propriétaire m'avait demandé au téléphone, en anglais, «Et depuis combien d'années habitez-vous Montréal??» (En d'autres mots, les immigrants n'étaient pas bienvenus...) Une autre fois, j'avais rencontré un type qui avait été concierge à Westmount. Il m'avait expliqué que, lorsqu'une famille noire essayait de louer un logement dans cette ville riche, le concierge était payé pour leur dire que tout était loué. Puis, en 1987, je travaillais pour un cabinet d'avocats à Montréal, Martineau Walker, et je m'étais aperçu que, sur 260 employés, il n'y avait que deux noirs, une secrétaire noire, et un homme de couleur qui arrosait les plantes. Alors j'avais demandé à un collègue traducteur si le cabinet avait une politique d'embauche raciste; il m'avait répondu que non, mais on pensait que les clients ne voudraient pas avoir affaire à des avocats noirs. Et il n'y avait aucune façon de prouver que le cabinet d'avocats était raciste, puisqu'on avait embauché une secrétaire de couleur!

Le philosophe palestinien Edward Saïd raconte comment on entretient cette ignorance. Il dit, par exemple, que si on comprend l'arabe, on peut déceler les faux sens et la fausse traduction des discours politiques en arabe! Si le traducteur qui traduit vers l'anglais fait dire n'importe quoi à un politicien comme Saddam Hussein, le gouvernement américain peut le faire passer pour un maudit fou et ainsi justifier l'invasion de l'Irak! Mais pour ceux qui ne parlent pas arabe, on gobe tout, et le tour est joué! Encore du maya, de l'illusion, de la duplicité, de la supercherie! Arjuna a beau ne pas comprendre que le champ de bataille est du maya, de l'illusion, mais c'est un roi – il est bien mal placé pour comprendre.

Le maire Drapeau à Montréal avait déclaré en public que la révolution tranquille au Québec avait été commencée par des professeurs algériens à l'Université de Montréal. Pourtant, n'importe qui ayant étudié l'histoire du Québec savait pertinemment que la révolution tranquille avait été lancée par le père dominicain Henri Lévesque, qui enseignait la sociologie à l'université. On sait combien avait pesé le manifeste Le Refus global, qu'avaient signé les artistes automatistes de l'époque. Et pourtant, mon père, comme tant d'autres, croyait au discours délirant de Jean Drapeau. On peut prétendre n'importe quoi, lorsqu'on est maire...

À la même époque, en 1969, le premier ministre Trudeau disait des choses semblables : les séparatistes allaient «avoir» nos femmes et nos enfants! C'est comme disait Voltaire : «Mentez, mentez, il en restera toujours quelque chose.» J'avais écrit une lettre au solliciteur général du Canada, qui était alors le député libéral Warren Allemand. Je lui avais demandé pourquoi la police n'utilisait pas des principes chrétiens dans ses affaires, pourquoi ils n'avaient aucun sens de la miséricorde. Et lui de me répondre que si, les agents de la police appliquaient toujours des principes justes et miséricordieux dans leurs démêlées avec le public! On dira que j'étais naïf de poser une telle question, mais j'avais envoyé une deuxième lettre au Ministre, lui demandant pourquoi alors la police avait menacé de me crever les yeux, de me poser des électrodes sur les testicules et de m'arracher les ongles, lorsque j'avais été interrogé en 1969. Il m'avait jeté de la poudre aux yeux, mais il n'a pas répondu à ma deuxième lettre... C'est d'ailleurs ce que m'avait révélé un toxicomane en 1972 ou 1973 : quand on demande des directions à un policier au coin des rues Peel et Sainte-Catherine, c'est une chose, mais c'est une autre paire de manches si la police entre de force chez vous parce qu'ils soupçonnent qu'il y a de l'héroïne dans votre logement...

Enfin, je comprends maintenant pourquoi il n'y a pas de

quartier arabe à Chambly, sur la rive Sud. Une résidente de la région m'avait parlé d'un enregistrement qu'elle avait vu. Il y avait un imam iranien qui déblatérait en disant que l'agenda secrète de tous les musulmans se réduisait à tuer tous les infidèles! C'était cela, le jihad. Je lui avais répondu qu'il fallait vérifier ce qu'avait dit le traducteur, car l'imam parlait en arabe et on pouvait lui faire dire n'importe quoi!

Il suffit de quelques mensonges de ce genre, puis vos enfants n'ont plus le droit de jouer avec les enfants des immigrants, n'est-ce pas? On n'embauche pas d'immigrants, on ne leur loue pas de logements, puis l'affaire est dans le sac, on a un quartier homogène, comme à Chambly, comme à Saint-Jean-sur-le-Richelieu. Mais l'orage gronde dans les médias : «ils vont nous avoir, les immigrants!» Puis on élit des partis xénophobes comme l'Action démocratique et le parti de Jean-Marie Le Pen, et le tour est presque joué. Sauf qu'il reste le spectre des immigrants, le spectre des Juifs et des Arabes à l'horizon.

Comme disait Karl Marx dans Le Manifeste : «Un spectre hante l'Europe, et ce spectre c'est le communisme!» Mais on s'est débarrassé des communistes en Europe, on a assassiné Saddam Hussein, Kadhafi, Ben Laden – le spectre demeure. Votre fille de dix-huit ans, va-t-elle épouser un Algérien?

V. LA PAIX DANS LE MONDE?

C'est autour de 1991. Un collègue à moi me sous-traite à traduire en français un document émanant du Pentagone au sujet des trains à haute vitesse. Voyons! Le Pentagone qui discute des trains? Mais si, le raisonnement de l'essai veut que la Guerre froide vient de se terminer et que l'occasion se présente de convertir les usines d'armes à des fins pacifiques. Ce serait merveilleux, n'est-ce pas? Les usines où l'on construit actuellement des chars d'assauts, des missiles et des avions chasseurs serviraient désormais à bâtir des trains à haute vitesse. Ensuite, on présente le sujet des trains à haute vitesse, qui flottent sur des aimants à un demi-pouce dans les airs et peuvent ainsi atteindre des vitesses de 160 milles à l'heure et davantage. On décrit l'expérience de ces trains au Japon et en Italie. L'essai démontre les avantages évidents de ces véhicules. Mais tout à coup, vers la fin de l'essai, les auteurs font des calculs et prouvent qu'il serait plus avantageux, plus rentable et plus profitable de continuer à créer des petites guerres au tiers monde et à vendre des armes à ces pays en guerre. Hélas! L'essai ne décrit pas le coût humain de ces guerres, en fonction des blessés et des morts, en fonction de la souffrance humaine. Le seul facteur qui pèse dans la balance, c'est l'argent... On peut voir aujourd'hui miroiter sur les parois de la caverne de Platon l'espoir de la paix mondiale. Toutefois, la décision a déjà été prise. Les jeux sont faits, rien ne va plus. La guerre crée des emplois. Krisna et Arjuna ne songent pas du tout aux facteurs économiques et au coût de la guerre. Tout ce que prétend Krisna, c'est que ce mélodrame de la guerre constante dans notre monde est du maya, de l'illusion. Krisna ne discute pas avec Arjuna au sujet de la propagande, du lessivage de cerveau et des machines à décerveler qu'utilisent les faiseurs de guerre pour recruter des soldats pour leurs armées et pour justifier ces massacres sanguinaires.

Mais aujourd'hui, Obama, le président américain, se rend compte du coût financier de poursuivre la guerre en Irak. Des milliers de dollars par minute, voire des millions, pour continuer cette guerre. Alors, étant rusé, il retire ses soldats de l'Irak et y envoie des mercenaires du type Blackwater. On retourne à l'époque des Croisades. La chanson de Roland. L'âge des ténèbres. Le malheur veut que les mercenaires ne soient aucunement responsables envers le public. Pour être admissible, il suffit d'être citoyen américain et d'avoir une cote sécuritaire en vigueur. La compagnie Blackwater est basée en partie sur l'Ordre des Templiers, qui a lutté contre les musulmans dans les Croisades au XIIème siècle. Il est aussi exigé des mercenaires Blackwater qu'ils aient de quatre à huit ans d'expérience dans l'armée et qu'ils ne soient ni endettés ni toxicomanes. Il y a des camps d'entraînement paramilitaires Blackwater un peu partout aux États-Unis, tout comme les bases Al Qaeda au Pakistan.

Krisna et Arjuna déambulent en char à travers les champs de bataille et remarquent sûrement les soldats, les mercenaires et les cadavres. Comme disait Napoléon Bonaparte dans ses écrits, il n'y a rien de semblable à l'odeur d'un champ de bataille le lendemain d'un massacre. Entre-temps, j'ai assisté à des manifs et à des émeutes, mais je n'ai jamais fait la guerre. Ce matin, je prenais mon café bien paisiblement en récitant mon chapelet, sous le soleil levant, assis sur mon balcon, et je regardais les démêlées entre les écureuils dans les arbres. Tout semblait normal – sauf que mon chat a attrapé et dévoré une grosse mouche.

Cet après-midi ma conjointe et moi avons pris l'auto pour aller chercher notre fille Isabelle, de vingt ans, qui voulait faire le lavage de son «chum» et à cinq heures, nous reprendrons l'auto pour aller chercher notre autre fille, Cordelia, de dix-huit ans, après sa journée de travail dans un centre d'achat. Hier soir, ma conjointe Bonnie et moi sommes allés à la bibliothèque nationale pour faire de la lecture puis prendre un café ensemble sur la rue St-Denis. Jésus avait prédit qu'on entendrait parler de guerres et de rumeurs de guerre. Pourtant tout est paisible dans notre vie, sauf lorsque les enfants s'énervent. Parfois, dans mon appartement, j'entends passer un camion de pompiers avec une sirène qui crie, mais aujourd'hui, tout est tranquille dans notre quartier.

Nous sommes entourés de guerres et de rumeurs de guerre. Krisna et Arjuna voient s'agiter le monde, et ses distractions. Comme disait Teilhard de Chardin, il y a tant d'énergie de gaspillée dans une soirée dans un centre-ville, dans les boîtes de nuit et les bars, sous les feux rutilants de minuit. Bonnie et moi habitons à l'écart du centre-ville, et nous tâchons de nous concentrer sur l'essentiel. Nous nous occupons de nos enfants, nous faisons du ménage, nous travaillons, nous nous couchons tôt – c'est plutôt un régime monastique! Bonnie va à la messe et moi je dis le chapelet. Tout cela à jeun : pas de tabac, pas d'alcool, pas de drogue. Nous laissons à d'autres les plaisirs de faire la guerre, de piller, de violer, de s'entretuer. Et nous ne courons pas après l'argent à tout prix… Quand ma mère est décédée, elle m'a laissé de l'argent, mais j'ai immédiatement placé tout le magot dans un compte de fiducie pour défrayer l'éducation de nos enfants, et au bout de quatre jours il restait assez pour nous acheter une pizza tout garnie. L'argent était placé, et je n'ai pas du tout fêté. J'ai aussi payé des comptes, comme mon impôt et le loyer pour quelques mois, mais je n'ai rien gaspillé. Bonnie aussi a hérité et elle gère ses placements et paie les comptes du ménage. On ne vit pas dans le luxe ou le plaisir fou.

Pourtant, il y avait une époque où j'étais plus jeune et je croyais avoir trente-cinq meilleurs amis; le fait est que je payais la traite à toutes sortes de parasites. À un j'achetais une bière; à l'autre, je payais un repas au restaurant. Je prenais des taxis partout, je mangeais tous mes repas au restaurant, je couraillais les femmes de rue, je dépensais follement dans les bars – et selon mon curriculum vitae, j'occupais des postes responsables dans les bureaux. J'étais complètement énervé. Ivre. Solitaire. Égoïste. Confus. La vie à la course. Un homme pressé.

Depuis cette période, j'ai cessé de boire et de consommer des substances. Ma première réaction, environ trois mois plus tard, a été que je me suis aperçu un bon matin que ma rage et ma colère étaient disparues. Maintenant, je n'ai pas bu depuis douze ans et je peux en réalité prendre le temps de réfléchir, sans me sentir forcé d'être d'accord avec un autre ou de faire plaisir à quiconque. Je ne suis plus toujours grisé et confus; je n'ai plus besoin de créer des illusions et du maya autour de moi; je ne me trouve pas particulièrement fin ou beau ou spirituel. Je ne passe plus mon temps à essayer d'être accepté par les gens de mon entourage. Plusieurs personnes me détestent à mort, et ça ne me dérange pas une miette. Je n'ai pas besoin de compenser pour mes ennemis ou de décompenser en faisant des scènes. Je commets beaucoup d'erreurs tous les jours, et je n'en suis pas gêné, je n'en ai pas honte. J'ai déjà passé des soirées assez désagréables merci beaucoup, à broyer du noir, mais cette période semble révolue. Il y a quelques principes spirituels assez simples qu'il faut suivre pour être heureux, quelques étapes à franchir.

Je ne connais pas Dieu intimement. Je ne pourrais ni le définir ni le décrire. Toutefois, c'est bien lui qui me guide d'une circonstance à l'autre, qui répond à tous mes besoins raisonnables par le truchement de mes semblables, qui me façonne tous les jours, un jour à la fois, puisque je lui demande de le faire. Il est comme un grand érable, et je suis une seule parmi les feuilles sur ses branches. Il me tient en vie, dans l'Amour avec un grand «A».

Je sais cependant que le concept du divin a été utilisé et manipulé par bien des escrocs de mauvaise foi, qui pensaient être quelque chose de spécial. La bête et le faux prophète ont mené toutes les sociétés de l'histoire. On a utilisé le nom de Dieu pour faire la guerre, piller, violer, faire des ravages. Qu'importe? Je sais que je n'utilise pas le nom de Dieu à mauvais escient. Pour moi, son nom est synonyme de respect, d'humilité et de bienveillance. Comme dit le proverbe, l'amour est enfant de la liberté.

Malheureusement, les œuvres de bienfaisance, les organismes à but non lucratif se sont accaparés du principe de la charité, de la solidarité. Ils nous présentent dans les médias des images de famine, de sécheresses, de maladie tirées du tiers monde, puis ils nous demandent une aumône. On sait que presque tout l'argent qu'on donne à ces œuvres va dans les frais administratifs et dans la poche des administrateurs. J'ai assez fait de bénévolat pour en être au courant. Mieux vaut donner directement à ceux et à celles qui sont dans le besoin. On commence par s'occuper de sa famille. Ensuite, on aide la personne qui demande de l'aide. Je connais plein de lascars qui travaillent pour les mille et une œuvres de bienfaisance pour s'enrichir personnellement.

Nous sommes tous des feuilles sur un arbre divin, l'arbre de la Vie. Serrons-nous les coudes et tenons-nous ensemble. À plusieurs, nous en viendrons à bout. Quand dix millions de personnes dans le monde entier ont manifesté en 2003 contre l'invasion de l'Irak, le gouvernement de George W. Bush ne nous a pas écoutés, mais nous savions que nous représentions encore plus de gens; c'était une des premières fois de l'histoire que tant de gens s'étaient inscrits en faux contre l'iniquité de la guerre. Il n'y a pas assez de prisons dans le monde pour enfermer autant de dissidents. Et le principe de base d'Amnistie Internationale est que lorsque les gouvernements emprisonnent injustement les gens, lorsqu'ils les torturent pour leurs idées, lorsque des dissidents sont enlevés et disparaissent, ces autorités le font à la cachette. En exposant ces actions au grand jour, on force les tortionnaires à libérer leurs victimes.

«Ils transformeront leurs épées en socs de charrue...et

les hommes ne feront plus la guerre.» Ce verset d'Ésaïe est la devise de l'ONU; il avait été proposé comme devise par l'URSS. Cependant, l'Organisation des Nations-Unies s'est avérée impuissante à mettre fin aux injustices et aux guerres, à cause du veto des Américains très souvent.

Des guerres et des rumeurs de guerre. Des ombres qui dansent sur les parois de la caverne de Platon. Du maya, de l'illusion. Quand sortira-t-on au grand jour pour contempler la vérité? Quand cessera-t-on d'écouter de la propagande meurtrière? Quand cesseront les invasions et le pillage au nom de la démocratie? Si l'on jette un coup d'œil rapidement à travers la porte de la caverne, on voit les manifestants passer. On voit l'espoir que les choses vont changer. Les mafiosi qui mènent le gouvernement vont finir par reculer. Au lieu de dépenser sur des armes, le gouvernement va finir par appuyer les artistes, les artisans de paix, les gens de bonne volonté. On va finir par convaincre les gens qui investissent dans le pétrole qu'on a seulement une planète, un environnement pour le genre humain. On pourra peut-être prévenir le prochain désastre écologique, le prochain déversement de pétrole dans l'océan. Oui, on pourra mettre fin à la guerre. Si on s'y met.

Juillet-août 2012

14. THRENODY

You walk down a country road, on a windy fall day; the leaves are circling around you, blown about by the augur of winter. You approach the gate of the abandoned garden where the corpses lie. Your hair is blowing in the wind, whipped around by every gust. You stick your hands deep into your coat pockets, just to keep your fingers warm. The fence surrounding the cemetery is dilapidated and dangling from loose nails. Some of the pickets lean on others, and there is a spirit of desolation all around you.

You enter the garden, walking through piles of dead leaves, which are brown and crackling under your feet. You make out the grey and brown scenery, despite the decay and disrepair of the tombstones lined up in death rows. Some of the crosses are no longer standing. And there are not only crosses here: there are monuments for people of other faiths. Winds of change blow in your cold face, announcing another season.

There are inscriptions on the tombstones, bearing the names of the dead buried under the frosty ground. Look, here is Dan Slote, who died a few years ago: you knew him in the eighties. He tried to help you along with your writing. And as you recognize his name, which is partly erased by time, you get a cramp in your chest. The tombstones here are not elaborate; they are wooden tombstones, nondescript, and plain. You would think there would be a monument here.

And here is another name you recognize, Julia Shreck, who came to an untimely end when she was in her mid-thirties. You knew her. She had such an unhappy life, and the only time you remember seeing her look joyful was when she was pregnant for Joshua Zoltan, her only son. You look up at the horizon, beyond the cemetery fence, and the setting sun is struggling to peek out through the grey, dishevelled clouds.

You walk along the rows, searching for other names you recognize. The upkeep of this holy place has been neglected. Look, here is Peter Brawley, with dates. You knew him as well; he died of a heart attack at age sixty-one. The inscription on his monument has also been partly erased over the past few years since he went into the beyond.

There are family members, whom you treasured: your mother, and your cousins Paul and Marjorie. Many of the tombstones have fallen.

You stuff your frostbitten hands deeper into your pockets. The wind howls from a distance. There is one lone dead tree just outside the garden. And you can hear the lonely wind rustling through the remaining leaves and the creaking of the branches, like the masts of a sailboat carrying the dead to another shore.

Really, it is too cold, and you walk back out of this morbid garden. You shuffle along the country road, back to the village, where the living are staying warm.

You can remember the dead, you can even talk to them, but the only response is the wind rushing past you, into the emptiness.

February 3rd, 2013

15. THIS DOPAMINE WORLD

It is four o'clock in the morning, and I am sitting in my small living room, while my wife and kids sleep. Beside my armchair, there is a mock fireplace, with Egyptian statuettes made in China on the mantle, mingling with crawling green plants. Since it is night time, I have lit a small lamp on top of the sewing table I inherited from my aunt Louise. The lampshade is yellowish, so the whole room is mirrored in the window opening on to the street. This reflection includes the dead maple tree outside our window. Actually, it is not dead, but it is just sleeping in mid-April. The tree in the window seems to be growing right inside the living room. Occasionally, a car passes on the street, and the reflection of the car's headlights flashes across the photograph on the wall.

So the photo contains dopamine tree branches. You may think this is an illusion, but at four in the morning, everything is real.

I remember being about eight years old, in Ottawa East, and delivering the newspapers along my paper route on Echo Drive in the dead of winter. A car would race past me; I knew it was shooting bullets at me with its headlights. Just like in the movies. And I would hide behind a snow bank along the sidewalk, and fire real bullets with my index finger at the passing vehicle.

I had a subscription to the Tintin magazine, and the adventures were interwoven with my grade school studies, with the nuns' teachings about Jesus, with my father's lies about his past. I would walk to school along Main Street and ward off the kidnappers and opium traffickers whom Tintin was fighting against.

And when my mother was ninety years old, some time later, I would phone her and she would tell me about her travels that day and that she had to return to her parents' house that evening. She would ask me to say a mass for her. I would answer, in French, "But Mom, you know I am not a priest. I have two daughters and I live with Bonnie." She would reply, "Stop pulling my leg. Just say a mass for me, will you?" And this charade would go on and on. This was long after I served mass as an eight year old boy. I would take the ritual very seriously. I had been chosen for the ministry. I wore my little cassock with gravity, and I held on tight to the candlestick I was holding. Yes, I am a priest.

I hadn't discovered girls yet. One day, while I was in seminary school, studying for the priesthood, I found a Playboy magazine in a phone booth. I found colour pictures of naked ladies of incredible beauty, stretching out in unreal positions, showing off their wonderful bodies, always with a knowing smile. This was paradise right here, right now. These women became my secret lovers, my best friends, my fantasy girlfriends.

Soon later, I was longing for a magical world beyond the restrictions of my parents' lives, and discovered drugs. I tried about three times before I managed to purchase some real LSD25. I kept purchasing sugar cubes that just contained sugar. Finally, I found the real thing, a whole other dimension was opened to my imagination, and I started thinking the hallucinations were real. They were, at the time.

Much later, my mid-life crisis was that I kicked the tobacco, the alcohol and the drugs. I imagined I got my life in order. By now, I dreamed I was raising a family and living responsibly. I had a semblance of realism in my thinking and could actually work and write and function like a normal person. My perceptions were no longer tainted with dopamine and daydreams and wishful thinking.

But tonight, at four in the morning, I am not so sure. There is still a blind spot in my rear-view mirror. I am still a lonely, alienated, depressed individual. I dream my wife loves me, my kids love me – but I am growing roots, and have lost my leaves, just like the tree growing inside my living room. I am ready for a dopamine resurrection into the next dream.

February 5, 2014

16. THE TRAIN TO NOWHERE

I saw a subway going nowhere, full of friends and relatives who had passed away, Franco's and Stalin's arguing vehemently, although I couldn't make out what they were saying, as the train went further and further down the tracks into oblivion, at least from here. As Albert Einstein says, our perception of time and space is relative to our point of view, and I could no longer see these dead people but I certainly went on hearing them in my head, in my heart and in little objects like symbols of them lying about the house, covered in yellow autumn leaves, dusty photographs for instance and home videos about the dead, about those who preceded us and made the same mistakes as us many times before. Partial stop. Pause. This subway was going deeper and deeper into the darkness of the subway tunnels, and we mentioned these dead people less and less often. Most of them died without making any noise, in a hospital ward, with a mask over their face, with tubes attached to their arms, nurses milling about unawares that one of these patients had made his getaway, committing the sin of jailbreak, leaving the rest of us prisoners of time and space very much connected to the seasons of our blindness and ignorance. Oh look, there goes a passenger of the subway, flying over the moon. The clouds of time swallowed him up quickly, didn't they? Meanwhile, newborns and teenagers launched off bravely into the fray, unconscious to a degree of the heartaches and broken limbs that awaited them as they boarded the subway into death. And by the time you have buried half your friends and most your family, you are all busted up and relieved to be leaving this place. Amen.

October 15, 2011

17. THE WHOLE WORLD
IN HIS HANDS

Last night, I understood the meaning of life. Boing. Just like that.

This is how it happened. Our twenty-one year old daughter Isabelle had the car for the evening. She had to work at the Collège de Montréal and it was agreed she would be back with the car by 11:00 o'clock. The reason she was supposed to be back at that time was that her sister Cordelia was invited to a party on Sainte-Catherine Street and my girlfriend and I were supposed to drive her there. We had agreed with Cordelia we would leave at 11:00. So we waited. Eleven o'clock rolled around and we waited some more. I was starting to get impatient. I was fuming in fact. I was telling myself that Isabelle wasn't getting the car all weekend. We kept phoning her and texting her and there was no answer. Finally she texted back that she had gone out for supper with her boyfriend Shayne and she would be back soon. And I am waiting and I am angry.

At long last, Isabelle shows up with the car at 11:40 p.m. She has her boyfriend and her boyfriend's dogs in the car with her. Now we know the landlord doesn't want dogs in our apartment, but we don't fuss. As Cordelia is getting into the car, so we can drive her to her appointment, a few sharp words are exchanged because Cordelia borrowed Isabelle's jacket. OK the dogs are cute. They are two Doberman puppies six weeks old that Isabelle and Shayne bought two weeks ago. But they are not allowed in our apartment.

So we leave anyway. Cordelia's party is at La Cage aux Sports near Sherbrooke and Atwater. Those are the only directions Cordelia gives us. We drive down one street and Cordelia says we have to go back home because she forgot her I.D. and her house keys. So we try to drive back and come up Earnscliffe from Monkland and the street is blocked because a tree has fallen in yesterday's wind storm. So Bonnie turns the car around with great difficulty on a narrow one-way street and we drive the wrong way down back to Monkland Avenue. Finally, we make it to our house. Cordelia gets out of the car, runs to the house and runs back to the car a minute later – and we take off. We are driving up The Boulevard in Westmount and keep getting red lights. I tell Bonnie, "It seems the gods are not with us…" I am not too happy with things. It is midnight and my daughter is going out for a drink and we don't know where she is going.

OK, we pull down Atwater and turn left on Sainte-Catherine. We go past the AMC Forum and suddenly, like a revelation, after all this frustration, despite all odds – Cordelia screams out, "Stop the car! There are Lauren and my friends on the sidewalk!" They were walking towards the bar -- they hadn't gotten there yet – if we had got there at 11:30 as we planned, her friends wouldn't have been there yet – the timing is just perfect!!

Cordelia gets out of the car, her friend James gives her a big hug, and there is Cordelia with four or five of her buddies, and everything worked out! And it occurs to me a few minutes later that maybe the whole universe is like that. We struggle, we suffer, we encounter opposition and contradiction, we create drama, -- and we don't know it, but we are right on time

November 2nd, 2013